AQA Physics

GCSE

Higher Workbook

Helen Reynolds

Darren Forbes

Editor: Lawrie Ryan

OXFORD

UNIVERSITY PRESS

Great Clarendon Street, Oxford, OX2 6DP, United Kingdom

Oxford University Press is a department of the University of Oxford.
It furthers the University's objective of excellence in research,
scholarship, and education by publishing worldwide. Oxford is a
registered trade mark of Oxford University Press in the UK and in
certain other countries

British Library Cataloguing in Publication Data
Data available

978 0 19 842169 6

10 9 8 7 6 5

Paper used in the production of this book is a natural, recyclable
product made from wood grown in sustainable forests.
The manufacturing process conforms to the environmental regulations
of the country of origin.

Printed in India by Multivista Global Pvt. Ltd.

Acknowledgements

Cover: Eric James Azure/Offset

p9: Chones/Shutterstock; **p71**: Jaruek Chairak/Shutterstock;
p109: Wang Song/Shutterstock.

Artwork by Q2A Media Service Ltd.

Contents

Introduction

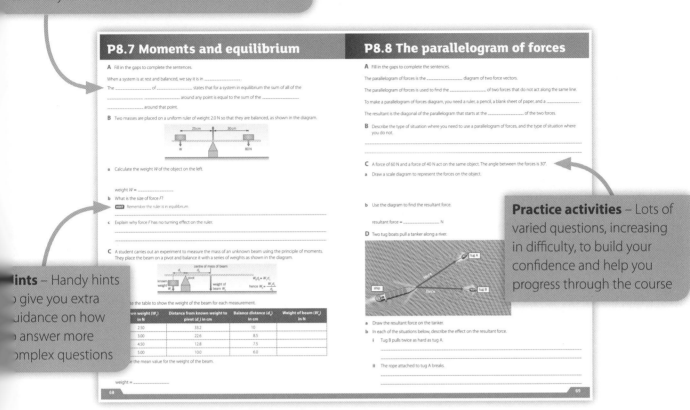

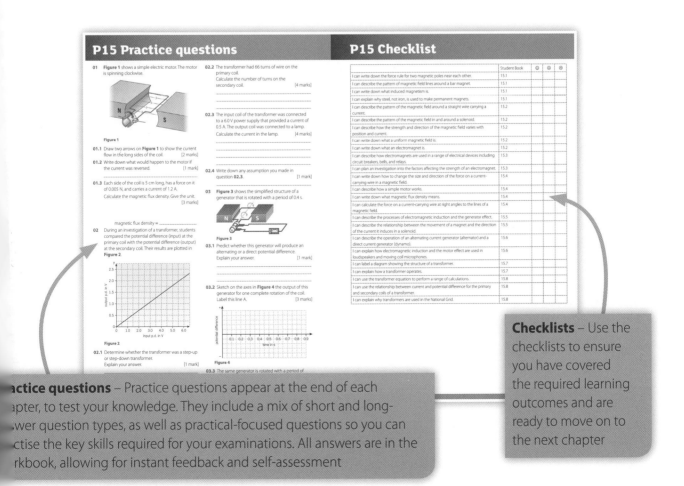

P1.1 Changes in energy stores

A Fill in the gaps to complete the sentences.

An energy _____ is a way of keeping track of energy.

You can transfer energy by _____ , by _____ , by _____ , and by _____ .

When an object falls, the energy in its _____ _____ energy store decreases, and the energy

in its _____ energy store increases.

When an object hits the ground but does not bounce, the energy in its _____ energy store

decreases. Energy is transferred to the _____ by sound waves and by _____ .

B There are different types of energy store. Give an example of an **activity** that you could do to make the change in each energy store described below.

a A decrease in the energy in the **chemical store** of a battery.

_____

_____

b An increase in the energy in a **gravitational potential store**.

_____

_____

c An increase in the energy in an **elastic potential store**.

_____

_____

C A wind-up torch produces light when you turn the handle.

Starting with when you eat food:

- describe the **changes in energy** in energy stores before and after you use the torch
- describe the **physical processes** that transfer energy between the stores.

_____

_____

_____

_____

_____

_____

_____

_____

P1.2 Conservation of energy

A Fill in the gaps to complete the sentences.

Energy cannot be _____ or _____ . This is the principle of _____ of energy,

which applies to _____ energy changes.

An isolated system is called a _____ system. There are no _____ transfers into or out of
the system.

If there are transfers within the system then the total energy does not _____ .

B On the Moon, there is no air. An astronaut on the Moon is holding a swinging pendulum. Energy transfers are
taking place.

Suggest what will happen to the motion and height of the pendulum over time. Explain whether or not the
pendulum is a closed system.

_____

_____

_____

_____

C What would happen if everyday situations became closed systems? Describe what you would observe in each of
the situations below.

a A bouncing ball.

_____

_____

b A child on a swing in motion.

_____

_____

c A bungee jumper.

_____

_____

d There is a roller coaster at a funfair.

Describe a system involving the rollercoaster that **is not** closed.

_____

_____

Describe a system involving the rollercoaster that **is** closed.

_____

_____

P1.3 Energy and work

A Fill in the gaps to complete the sentences.

'Work' in science is about using a _____ to move an object. Work is a way of _____ energy between energy stores.

You can calculate work using this equation:

work done (_____) = _____

[You need to remember this equation.]

When an object moves through the air it does work against _____, or when you slide it

across the floor it does work against _____ .

These processes _____ the surroundings.

B Calculate the **work** that a father does against friction when he pushes the buggy 180 m using a force of 15 N.

15 N

work done = _____

C Complete the table by calculating the work done by each force.

Force	Distance	Work
10 N	2 m	
30 N	10 cm	
25 kN	5 m	
20 kN	50 mm	

D A student uses a newton-meter to pull a tub full of sand across the floor. She wants to investigate how the mass of sand affects the work done against friction.

● Identify the independent, dependent, and control variables in this investigation.

● Describe and explain the measurements that the student needs to make and how she would use these measurements to find out how the mass of sand affects the work done against friction.

_____

_____

_____

_____

_____

_____

_____

P1.4 Gravitational energy stores

A Fill in the gaps to complete the sentences.

The gravitational potential energy of an object _____ when it is lifted up and _____ when it is moved down.

You do _____ when you lift something up to overcome the gravitational _____ .

The gravitational field strength on the Moon is _____ than it is on the Earth, so it is _____ to lift an object up on the Moon than on the Earth.

You can calculate the change in the gravitational potential energy store using this equation:

gravitational potential energy (_____) = _____

[You need to remember this equation.]

B There is a change in the gravitational potential energy store when you lift a suitcase into a car. The suitcase has a mass of 30 kg. You lift it up 1 m. Gravitational field strength = 10 N/kg.

Calculate the change in the gravitational potential energy store. Remember to include units.

change in gravitational potential energy = _____

C Complete the table by calculating the change in gravitational potential energy for each object.

Mass of object	Gravitational field strength in N/kg	Change in height	Change in gravitational potential energy store in J
1 kg	10	2 m	
1 kg	1.6	10 cm	
250 g	27	5 m	
20 g	10	50 mm	

D In the investigation described in Topic **P1.3**, activity **D**, a student pulled a tub of sand across the floor. Now the student wants to investigate pulling the same tub of sand up a ramp.

- Compare the type of work done in the two investigations.
- The distance travelled in each investigation is the same. Explain which amount of work done would be bigger.

_____

_____

_____

_____

_____

_____

_____

A Fill in the gaps to complete the sentences.

The kinetic energy of an object depends on its _____ and its _____ .

You can calculate kinetic energy using this equation:

kinetic energy (_____) = _____

[You need to remember this equation.]

When you stretch or compress an object, you do _____ and transfer energy to an _____ store.

[You can use this equation on the Physics equation sheet to calculate the change in elastic potential energy:
elastic potential energy = 0.5 × spring constant (N/kg) × (extension (m))^2]

B A student uses light gates to find the speed of a ball just before it hits the ground. He finds that the speed is 12.5 m/s. The mass of the ball is 50 g.

a Calculate the kinetic energy.

kinetic energy = _____

b The ball bounces. There is a point at which all the energy in the kinetic store of the ball is transferred to an elastic store. Write down what the ball is doing at this point.

_____

c Explain why the student needed to use light gates.

_____

_____

C A machine that throws tennis balls contains a spring with a spring constant of 145 N/m. When you push a ball into the machine, the spring compresses by 1.5 cm. The mass of the ball is 55 g.

Calculate the speed of the ball as it leaves the machine when you fire it.

speed of the ball = _____

P1.6 Energy dissipation

A Fill in the gaps to complete the sentences.

Useful energy is energy transferred in a pathway that we _____ .

In any device or process energy spreads out, which we call _____ .

Energy that is not useful is _____ . This energy is eventually transferred to the

_____ , which become _____ .

B For each of the activities below, describe **two** pathways that **dissipate** energy.

a Riding a bicycle.

_____

_____

b Using an electric drill.

_____

_____

c Using an electric kettle.

_____

_____

C On a car journey, there are lots of energy transfers. A student says that when you are travelling on a motorway at a steady speed of 60 mph, the energy in the chemical store of the fuel is being transferred to a kinetic store by the car's engine.

a Explain why this statement is wrong.

_____

_____

b Describe what happens to the energy in the fuel while a car is travelling at a steady speed.

_____

_____

c Suggest and explain whether the energy transfers that you have described in part **b** involve **useful energy** or **wasted energy**.

_____

_____

_____

_____

D You turn an electric heater on to heat a room. An hour later you turn it off. Describe this situation using the key words for this topic in the Student Book.

_____

_____

_____

_____

P1.7 Energy and efficiency

A Fill in the gaps to complete the sentences.

You can calculate efficiency using this equation:

$$\text{efficiency} = \frac{\rule{6cm}{0.4pt}}{\rule{5cm}{0.4pt}}$$

[*You need to remember this equation.*]

No device can be more than _____ % efficient, because this would mean that energy has been _____ .

Machines waste energy because of _____ between moving parts, by _____ the air when

they are moving, and by getting _____ when a current flows. You can reduce the amount of wasted

energy by _____ the surfaces between moving parts.

B **a** A motor has an input energy transfer of 1000 J and a useful output energy transfer of 400 J.
Calculate the **efficiency**.

efficiency = _____

b Calculate the input energy transfer required for the motor to transfer 25 J of useful output energy.

input energy transfer = _____

C Using an electric drill wastes a lot of energy. Suggest and explain how to improve the efficiency of a drill. Include
three processes that waste energy and **two** ways to reduce the energy wasted.

_____

_____

_____

_____

_____

_____

D A student says that a ball that does not bounce very high is not very efficient. Is she correct? Explain why.

_____

_____

_____

_____

_____

P1.8 Electrical appliances

A Fill in the gaps to complete the sentences.

Most of the energy that people use in their homes is supplied by gas, _____, or electricity.

_____ is a clean and efficient way of transferring energy to many of the appliances that you use every

day. You use electrical appliances for _____ (e.g., in an oven), _____ (e.g., a low-energy

lamp), moving objects (e.g., the turntable in a _____ oven), and creating sound and images.

More efficient electrical appliances waste _____ energy than less-efficient electrical devices.

B You can use an electric kettle or an oven to heat water. In each case, energy is transferred to the thermal store of the water.

Using the idea of efficiency, explain why you usually use a kettle and not an oven to heat water.

_____

_____

_____

C Here are some data about different types of light bulb. The bulbs appear equally bright.

Light bulb	Energy supplied to light bulb in 1 minute
X	700 J
Y	2500 J

a Identify the light bulb that is more efficient. _____

b Explain why you did not need to do a calculation to work out the answer to part **a**.

_____

_____

c Identify the light bulb that wastes more energy. _____

d Explain your answer to part **c**.

_____

_____

D You are shopping for an electrical appliance. To help you choose between different appliances, you compare the different prices.

Explain why you also need to compare power and efficiency when choosing an appliance.

_____

_____

_____

_____

_____

_____

_____

_____

P1.9 Energy and power

A Fill in the gaps to complete the sentences.

Power is the _____ of energy transfer.

You can calculate power using this equation:

$$\text{power} = \frac{\underline{\hspace{2cm}} \; (\underline{\hspace{1cm}})}{\underline{\hspace{2cm}} \; (\underline{\hspace{1cm}})}$$ **[You need to remember this equation.]**

You can calculate efficiency as a percentage using this equation:

$$\text{percentage efficiency} = \frac{\underline{\hspace{5cm}}}{\underline{\hspace{5cm}}} \; \underline{\hspace{1.5cm}}$$

[You need to remember this equation.]

You can calculate the power that is wasted using this equation:

power wasted = _____ power in – _____ power out

B A student says that more powerful devices are more efficient.

Explain why this is not always true.

_____

_____

C A lift carries you to the top floor of a building, transferring 170 kJ of energy in 15 seconds.

a Calculate the useful power output of the lift.

      useful power = _____ W

b The total power in is 20 kW.

    Calculate the percentage efficiency of the lift.

      efficiency = _____ %

c Calculate the wasted power.

      wasted power = _____ W

P1 Practice questions

01 You drop a ball and it bounces as shown in **Figure 1**.

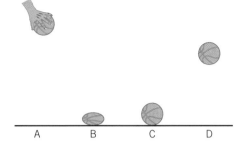

Figure 1

01.1 Describe the changes in energy between points **A** and **B**. [2 marks]

_____

_____

01.2 Explain why the ball reaches a lower height when it bounces. [1 mark]

_____

_____

02 A scientist measures the time it takes two kettles with the same power rating to boil water. **Table 1** shows the data from the experiment.

Table 1

Kettle	Energy required to boil water in J	Energy supplied to kettle in J
A	300 000	400 000
B	300 000	450 000

02.1 Describe how the scientist calculated the energy suppled to the kettle. [2 marks]

_____

_____

02.2 Identify **one** control variable in this experiment. [1 mark]

_____

02.3 Calculate the efficiency of kettle **A**. Write down the equation that you will use. [3 marks]

_____

_____

_____

02.4 A manufacturer's kettles all have the same power rating. The manufacturer wants to make one kettle more efficient than the rest. Suggest how it could do this. [1 mark]

_____

03 About 100 years ago there was an event in the Olympic Games called the standing high jump. An athlete stood still, then jumped vertically. The world record is 1.9 m.

03.1 If the mass of the athlete is 50 kg, and gravitational field strength is 10 N/kg, calculate the take-off speed of the athlete. Write down the equations that you will use. [4 marks]

_____

_____

_____

_____

_____

03.2 Just before landing, the athlete has a speed of 6 m/s. Explain the difference between the take-off and landing speeds. [1 mark]

_____

_____

04 **Table 2** shows some data about the lifts in two very tall buildings. Compare the lifts when each lift is carrying 10 people, each with a mass of 70 kg, from the ground floor to the top of each building. Use ideas about work, power, and useful and wasted energy.
Gravitational field strength = 10 N/kg. [6 marks]

Table 2

	Empire State Building	The Shard
number of floors to observation floor	86	70
height of one floor	3 m	3 m
time to reach the observation floor	55 seconds	1 minute
efficiency of lift motor	85%	90%

_____

_____

_____

_____

_____

_____

_____

_____

_____

_____

_____

P1 Checklist

	Student Book	☺	😐	☹
I can describe the ways in which energy can be stored.	1.1			
I can describe how energy can be transferred.	1.1			
I can describe the energy transfers that happen when an object falls.	1.1			
I can describe the energy transfers that happen when a falling object hits the ground without bouncing back.	1.1			
I can describe what conservation of energy is.	1.2			
I can explain why conservation of energy is a very important idea.	1.2			
I can describe what a closed system is.	1.2			
I can describe energy transfers in a closed system.	1.2			
I can describe what work means in science.	1.3			
I can describe how work and energy are related.	1.3			
I can calculate the work done by a force.	1.3			
I can describe what happens to work that is done to overcome friction.	1.3			
I can describe what happens to the gravitational potential energy store of an object when it moves up or down.	1.4			
I can explain why an object moving up increases its gravitational potential energy store.	1.4			
I can explain why it is easier to lift an object on the Moon than on the Earth.	1.4			
I can calculate the change in gravitational potential energy of an object when it moves up or down.	1.4			
I can write down what the kinetic energy of an object depends on.	1.5			
I can calculate kinetic energy.	1.5			
I can describe what an elastic potential energy store is.	1.5			
I can calculate the amount of energy in an elastic potential energy store.	1.5			
I can describe what is meant by useful energy.	1.6			
I can describe what is meant by wasted energy.	1.6			
I can describe what eventually happens to wasted energy.	1.6			
I can describe if energy is still as useful after it is used.	1.6			
I can describe what is meant by efficiency.	1.7			
I can write down the maximum efficiency of any energy transfer.	1.7			
I can describe how machines waste energy.	1.7			
I can describe how energy is supplied to homes.	1.8			
I can explain why electrical appliances are useful.	1.8			
I can describe what most everyday electrical appliances are used for.	1.8			
I can explain how to choose an electrical appliance for a particular job.	1.8			
I can describe what is meant by power.	1.9			
I can calculate the power of an appliance.	1.9			
I can calculate the efficiency of an appliance in terms of power.	1.9			
I can calculate the power wasted by an appliance.	1.9			

A Fill in the gaps to complete the sentences.

The best conductors of energy are _____ . Materials such as wool and fibreglass, which are

_____ , are good insulators.

A material with a high thermal conductivity has a _____ rate of energy transfer through it.

The thicker a layer of insulating material, the _____ the rate of energy transfer through it.

B The diagram shows an experiment to investigate conduction. The wax on rod **X** melts first, then the wax on rod **Z**, and finally the wax on rod **Y**.

a Name the rods in order of thermal conductivity, starting with the **lowest**.

_____

b Describe how you worked out the answer to part **a**.

_____

_____

c Suppose you had two rods with similar thermal conductivities. Suggest and explain **two** improvements to this experiment that would help you tell the difference between the two rods.

_____

_____

_____

_____

d Loft insulation needs to trap lots of air. Explain what this tells you about the thermal conductivity of the loft insulation material compared with the thermal conductivity of air.

_____

_____

_____

_____

_____

P2.2 Infrared radiation

A Fill in the gaps to complete the sentences.

Infrared radiation forms one part of the _____ _____ that _____ be detected

by our eyes. Infrared radiation has a _____ wavelength than visible light.

All objects emit infrared radiation. The _____ the temperature, the _____ the rate of emission.

An object at a particular temperature emits radiation across a _____ _____ of wavelengths.

As the temperature of the object increases, the _____ of the radiation it emits increases at all

_____ .

B Describe how infrared radiation can be detected.

HINT Think about how your body could detect it and what instruments could be used.

_____

_____

_____

C Describe the properties of a 'perfect black body', in relation to radiation.

_____

_____

_____

_____

D The graph shows the intensity of different wavelengths of radiation emitted by an object at two different temperatures.

a Which curve shows the object at a higher temperature? Circle **X** or **Y** on the graph below.

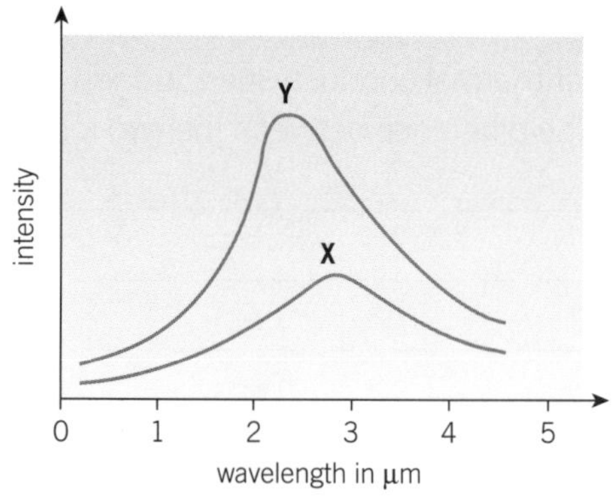

b Describe the differences between the radiation emitted by the object at the two different temperatures and how the object might appear different at these temperatures.

HINT Compare the peaks and the overall area under the graphs. What does the area represent?

_____

_____

_____

_____

_____

P2.3 More about infrared radiation

A Fill in the gaps to complete the sentences.

All objects _____ and _____ infrared radiation, no matter what their temperature.

When an object is at a constant _____ this means that these two processes are happening at the

_____ _____ .

Absorption and emission of infrared radiation by the Earth's _____ affects the temperature of the Earth's

surface. The _____ of the infrared radiation emitted by the surface of the Earth is _____

than the wavelength of the infrared radiation absorbed by the Earth from the Sun.

Molecules of water vapour, methane, and _____ _____ gas _____ the infrared

radiation emitted by the ground and this causes the temperature of the atmosphere to _____ . Together

these gases are known as _____ gases.

B An ice-cold can of fizzy drink is taken from the freezer and placed in direct sunlight.

Describe and explain the temperature change of the can over a period of several hours.

_____

_____

_____

_____

_____

C Complete the table to compare the emission and absorption of infrared radiation by the surface of the Earth and by greenhouse gases in the atmosphere, during daytime and night-time.

Describe differences in the amounts and the wavelength of the radiation emitted and absorbed.

	Surface of the Earth	Gases in the atmosphere
Daytime		
Night-time		

D The presence of a small proportion of greenhouse gases in the Earth's atmosphere helps to keep the temperature of most of the surface of the Earth suitable for habitation.

Describe how these atmospheric greenhouse gases help to maintain the Earth's average temperature.

_____

_____

_____

_____

_____

_____

P2.4 Specific heat capacity

A Fill in the gaps to complete the sentences.

The specific heat capacity is the energy needed to change the temperature of _____ of a substance by

_____ °C.

Using a heater with the same rate of energy transfer, a more massive piece of a substance will take _____ to heat up than a less massive piece of the same substance.

To find the specific heat capacity you need to measure the _____ using a joulemeter, the temperature

difference using a _____, and the _____ using a digital balance.

[*You can use this equation on the Physics equation sheet to calculate the change in thermal energy*:
change in thermal energy (J) = mass (kg) × specific heat capacity (J/kg °C) × change in temperature (°C)]

B Look at the amounts of energy in the table below.

The specific heat capacity of aluminium is 900 J/kg °C, and the specific heat capacity of water is 4200 J/kg °C.

	Energy required to...
X	raise the temperature of 2 kg of aluminium by 20 °C
Y	raise the temperature of 1 kg of water by 20 °C
Z	raise the temperature of 1 kg of water by 10 °C

Write the letters in order from the smallest to the largest amount of energy, and explain how you worked out the order:

_____

_____

_____

C The samples in activity **B** are heated with an immersion heater with a power of 100 W. Compare the times taken to heat samples **X** and **Z**.

_____

_____

D A student puts 0.25 kg of water in an insulated beaker. She puts a heater in the beaker and switches it on. It raises the temperature of the water by 11.5 °C in 15 minutes.

a Calculate the change in thermal energy.

The specific heat capacity of water is 4200 J/kg °C.

change in thermal energy = _____ J

b Suggest what the student would notice if she used twice as much water.

_____

P2.5 Heating and insulating buildings

A Fill in the gaps to complete the sentences.

People use heaters that run on electricity or _____ to heat their homes, or central heating that runs on

_____ or gas. Solid fuel such as coal or _____ is often burned in stoves for heating.

People can reduce the energy transfer from the loft of a house using _____ _____ .
They can reduce the rate of energy transfer through windows using _____ _____ .

There are usually _____ layers of brick in the walls of a house, with a layer of _____

_____ insulation to reduce the rate of energy transfer. It also helps to use bricks on the outside that are

_____ and have a _____ thermal conductivity.

B Here are some fuels and some energy transfer devices used for heating in people's homes.

Tick the boxes to show which fuels each type of device may use. Each device may use more than one fuel.

Fuel	✓ if it may be burned in a stove	✓ if it may be used in a central heating system	✓ if it may be burned on a fire
oil			
coal or wood			
gas			

C **a** Describe what cavity wall insulation is, and refer to its thermal conductivity.

_____

_____

b Name **one** other method of insulating a house that works the **same** way as cavity wall insulation.
Explain your choice.

_____

_____

c Name **one** method of insulating a house that works in a **different** way to cavity wall insulation.
Explain your choice.

_____

_____

D A family is deciding between installing double glazing or loft insulation.

Double glazing costs £2000, and would save the family £100 per year on their heating bills.

Loft insulation costs £175, and would save them £25 per year on their heating bills.

They want the one with the lowest costs over a 30-year period. Which would you recommend that they choose?

_____

_____

_____

_____

_____

_____

P2 Practice questions

01 Some students test takeaway coffee cups to see which colour of cup will keep the coffee inside hotter for longer.

They put an equal volume of hot water at 70 °C into three different cups, X, Y, and Z, each having a lid. They placed them on a well-insulated surface but with their sides exposed to the air. They measured the temperature of the water 15 minutes later. Their results are shown in **Table 1**.

Table 1

	Cup colour	Temperature after 15 mins in °C
X	black	40
Y	shiny silver	55
Z	white	52

01.1 Identify the cup from which the least energy was transferred to the surroundings.
Circle the letter in the table. [1 mark]

01.2 Suggest why the containers were placed on a well-insulated surface. [1 mark]

01.3 Suggest and explain **one** other variable that the students need to control in this experiment. [2 marks]

02 **Figure 1** shows some equipment that you could use to measure the specific heat capacity of a substance.

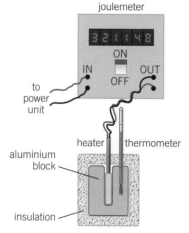

Figure 1

02.1 Explain why you need to insulate the aluminium block. [1 mark]

02.2 A student makes the following measurements using an insulated aluminium block.
temperature rise = 20 °C   mass of block = 1 kg
energy transferred = 45 J
Use these measurements to calculate the specific heat capacity of aluminium. Use this equation:
$$\text{specific heat capacity (J/kg °C)} = \frac{\text{energy (J)}}{\text{mass (kg)} \times \text{temperature change (°C)}}$$
[2 marks]

02.3 The student does the same experiment, but this time does not insulate the block. Explain what would happen to the student's measurement of the specific heat capacity of the uninsulated block. [2 marks]

03 In an article published in 1955, a scientist suggested that keeping someone at a comfortable sleeping temperature inside a sleeping bag depends on the thickness of the insulation of the bag.

Table 2

Temperature outside the sleeping bag in °C	Temperature difference between human body and outside the sleeping bag in °C	Thickness of the sleeping bag insulation in mm
4	33	38
−7	44	51
−18	55	64
−29	66	76
−40	77	89

03.1 Use the data from **Table 2** to show that the thickness of insulation needed for the sleeping bag is **proportional** to the difference between the temperature of the body inside the sleeping bag and the temperature outside the bag. [2 marks]

03.2 Explain why a modern sleeping bag designed for use at −40 °C is much thinner than 89 mm. [2 marks]

P2 Checklist

	Student Book	☺	☺	☹
I can write down which materials make the best conductors.	2.1			
I can write down which materials make the best insulators.	2.1			
I can describe how the thermal conductivity of a material affects the rate of energy transfer through it by conduction.	2.1			
I can describe how the thickness of a layer of material affects the rate of energy transfer through it by conduction.	2.1			
I can describe what the specific heat capacity of a substance means.	2.1			
I can explain why an object changes temperature due to emission and absorption of infrared radiation.	2.2			
I can describe the properties of a 'perfect black body'.	2.2			
I can describe how greenhouse gases affect the temperature of the Earth.	2.3			
I can calculate the energy needed to change the temperature of an object.	2.4			
I can describe how the mass of a substance affects how quickly its temperature changes when you heat it.	2.4			
I can describe how to measure the specific heat capacity of a substance.	2.4			
I can describe how homes are heated.	2.4			
I can describe how you can reduce the rate of energy transfer from your home.	2.5			
I can describe what cavity wall insulation is.	2.5			

P3.1 Energy demands

A Fill in the gaps to complete the sentences.

We meet most of our energy demands by burning _____, _____, and _____ .

These energy resources are non-renewable which means that they _____ run out.

Renewable resources _____ _____ run out.

Renewable fuels from living or recently living material are called _____ . One example is a gas called

_____ , and another example is a liquid called _____ .

We use uranium or plutonium in a _____ power station. These fuels release much _____ energy per kilogram than fossil fuels.

B We use energy resources for heating, transportation, and generating electricity.

a Suggest **one** fuel that could be used for all three purposes. _____

b Suggest **one** fuel that is used mainly for heating. _____

C a Describe what is meant by a biofuel.

_____

_____

b Explain why a biofuel is called renewable.

_____

_____

D a Explain why uranium atoms can be used to generate energy in nuclear power stations.

_____

b We can generate electricity with nuclear fuel or biofuels. The table below shows some information about the energy released by each kilogram of uranium that undergoes fission (fissile uranium) and a biofuel.

Fuel	Energy released per kg in MJ
fissile uranium	77 000 000
biofuel (animal manure)	12

i Calculate the mass of fissile uranium needed to release the same amount of energy as 1 tonne (1000 kg) of animal manure.

_____

_____

_____

ii Only 0.7% of uranium metal is fissile.

Calculate the mass of uranium metal that is needed to release the same amount of energy as 1 kg of animal manure.

_____

_____

_____

_____

P3.2 Energy from wind and water

A Fill in the gaps to complete the sentences.

A wind _____ is an electricity generator on top of a tall tower.

A _____ generator is used to generate electricity from wave power.

Water stored in lakes or reservoirs can run downhill, flowing through _____ that turn generators. This is

called _____ power.

In a _____ power station, water at high tide is trapped behind a barrage, then released to turn a generator.

Wind and wave power can be unreliable, and renewable resources can damage the _____ .

B **a** Both geothermal power and tidal power are renewable. Describe **one** similarity between geothermal power
and tidal power, using the idea of how electricity is generated.

_____

_____

  b Both wind power and wave power are renewable. Describe **one** similarity between wind power and wave
power, using the idea of how electricity is generated.

_____

_____

C One of the first hydroelectric power stations was at Niagara Falls in the USA.

Describe what happens in a hydroelectric power station.

_____

_____

_____

D The table shows the total cost per MW for different power stations that
use water.

Use the information in the table, and what you have learnt about the cost
of building power stations, to suggest **one** reason for each of the following
statements.

Power station	Total cost in £ per MW
hydroelectric	50
tidal	300
wave	100

  Hydroelectric power is cheapest: _____

_____

_____

_____

  Tidal power is more expensive than wave power:

_____

_____

_____

P3.3 Power from the Sun and the Earth

A Fill in the gaps to complete the sentences.

We use solar cells to _____ _____. They produce _____ amounts of

electricity, so you need lots of them. They are _____ to buy, and cost _____ to run.

We use solar heating panels to _____ water directly.

A solar power tower uses _____ to focus sunlight onto a water tank to produce steam, which can

generate _____.

Deep in the Earth, energy is released by _____ substances. This heats _____ that is pumped

deep down into the rocks. The water turns to _____, which drives _____ at the Earth's surface

to generate electricity.

B Compare a solar heating panel, a solar cell panel, and a solar power tower.

_____

_____

_____

_____

C Describe **two** advantages and **four** disadvantages of using solar cells to generate electricity.

_____

_____

_____

_____

_____

_____

D a A student makes a statement about power stations. Explain whether you agree.

'A nuclear power station is like a geothermal power station because both use radioactivity.'

_____

_____

_____

b Explain why geothermal power stations may not be an alternative to fossil fuel power stations in
some locations.

_____

_____

_____

P3.4 Energy and the environment

A Fill in the gaps to complete the sentences.

Burning fossil fuels releases _____ gases, which could cause global _____ . It also releases

sulfur dioxide, which can produce _____ _____ .

Nuclear fuels produce _____ energy per kilogram of fuel than fossil fuels, but also produce

_____ waste. Nuclear power stations are _____ to decommission, and dangerous if there is

an accident.

Renewable energy resources _____ _____ produce harmful waste products, and they can be

used in _____ places. However, they can take up a large area and disturb the habitats of _____ and

_____ . They can be _____ to manufacture or install.

B Describe **two** ways to reduce the environmental impact of coal-fired power stations.

_____

_____

C The table shows some disadvantages of renewable energy sources.

Tick the correct columns to show which renewable resources each disadvantage applies to. You may need to tick
several columns for each disadvantage.

Disadvantage	Wind?	Tidal?	Hydro?	Solar?
can cause noise pollution				
can affect river estuaries and the habitats of plants and animals there				
depends on the weather to work				
involves large reservoirs of water, which can affect the habitats of plants and animals				
needs large areas of land to produce enough energy from these panels				
not always available on demand				

D An island community wants to build a single power station to meet its electricity demand. Explain each of the
following, using the idea of the environment:

why a nuclear power station would be better than a fossil fuel power station.

_____

_____

_____

_____

why a fossil fuel power station would be better than a nuclear power station.

_____

_____

_____

_____

P3.5 Big energy issues

A Fill in the gaps to complete the sentences.

The demand for electricity varies over the day, and during the year. You can meet this demand with _____

fired power stations and _____ storage. Nuclear power stations are _____ to build, run, and

_____ (dismantle when you no longer need them).

The carbon dioxide produced by burning fuels can be removed from the atmosphere in a process called

_____ _____, but this is very expensive. Renewable resources are _____ to run

but _____ to install. We are going to need a range of resources to meet future demand for energy.

B Look at the graph showing the demand for electricity during a typical day.

a Suggest what 'base load' means.

_____

_____

_____

b Suggest how excess energy is stored.

_____

_____

_____

c Explain why this graph indicates that solar power cannot be relied upon to meet demand during the day.

_____

_____

C a Describe the difference between the capital costs and the running costs of a power station.

_____

_____

_____

b Suggest what might happen in the future to the capital costs of renewable energy resources.

_____

_____

D The capital costs of a nuclear power station and an offshore wind farm are about the same, but the total costs of the nuclear power station are half the total costs of the wind farm. Suggest why.

_____

_____

_____

_____

P3 Practice questions

01 Our energy demands can be met using a variety of fuels and energy resources.

01.1 Write down the **three** main fuels that we use today. [1 mark]

_____

01.2 Electricity can be generated using wind, waves, and tides. Tick the columns in **Table 1** that apply to each of these resources. You may need to tick more than one column for each resource. [3 marks]

Table 1

Type of resource	Uses water to turn a turbine	Uses air to turn a turbine	A turbine turns a generator	Reliable resource
wind				
waves				
tides				

02 Starting with uranium fuel rods, describe how a nuclear power station generates electricity. [6 marks]

_____
_____
_____
_____
_____
_____

03 **Figure 1** is a pie chart that shows the sources we currently use to generate electricity in the UK.

other fuels 5% and renewables
oil 1%
hydro 1%
nuclear 16%
coal 31%
gas 46%

Figure 1

3.1 Calculate the percentage of the UK's electricity that comes from fossil fuels. [2 marks]

_____
_____

3.2 Compare and contrast the effects on the environment of burning biofuels and fossil fuels. [4 marks]

_____
_____
_____
_____

3.3 Name an energy source in **Figure 1** that is in the category 'renewables'. [1 mark]

03.4 Write down **one** advantage and **one** disadvantage of using the energy source named in **03.3**. [2 marks]

_____
_____
_____

04 Dev and Sasha are arguing about which energy resources we should use in the future to generate electricity.
Write down the answer each person would give to the other. Include **two** reasons in each box. [4 marks]

Dev says: I think we should use nuclear power. It is reliable and doesn't produce greenhouse gases.	**Sasha's reply:**
Sasha says: I think we should use renewables. They are cheaper and better for the environment.	**Dev's reply:**

05 Solar panels save energy.

05.1 Give the **two** types of solar panel you can use on the roof of a house. [2 marks]

_____

05.2 There are about 25 million houses in the UK, and the area of each roof is about 140 m². The maximum output of a solar cell on a roof is about 250 W/m². Calculate the percentage of UK houses that would need to cover their roofs in solar cells to meet the UK base load of 5500 MW. [4 marks]

_____
_____
_____
_____
_____

05.3 Comment on the assumptions that you used in your calculation in **05.2**. Include an evaluation of the feasibility of powering the UK using solar cells. [4 marks]

_____
_____
_____
_____

P3 Checklist

	Student Book	☺	😐	☹
I can describe how most energy demands are met today.	3.1			
I can name the energy resources that are used.	3.1			
I can describe how nuclear fuels are used in power stations.	3.1			
I can name the other fuels that are used to generate electricity.	3.1			
I can describe what a wind turbine is made up of.	3.2			
I can describe how waves can be used to generate electricity.	3.2			
I can name the type of power station that uses water running downhill to generate electricity.	3.2			
I can describe how the tides can be used to generate electricity.	3.2			
I can describe what solar cells are and how they are used.	3.3			
I can describe the difference between a panel of solar cells and a solar heating panel.	3.3			
I can describe what geothermal energy is.	3.3			
I can describe how geothermal energy can be used to generate electricity.	3.3			
I can describe what fossil fuels do to the environment.	3.4			
I can explain why people are concerned about nuclear power.	3.4			
I can describe the advantages and disadvantages of renewable energy resources.	3.4			
I can evaluate the use of different energy resources.	3.4			
I can describe how best to use electricity supplies to meet variations in demand.	3.5			
I can compare the economic costs of different energy resources.	3.5			
I can name energy resources that need to be developed to meet people's energy needs in the future.	3.5			

P4.1 Electrical charges and fields

A Fill in the gaps to complete the sentences.

The nucleus of an atom is made from two types of particle: _____ and _____ . Particles

called _____ move around outside this nucleus.

In an _____ atom there are an equal number of protons and electrons. When electrons are

transferred to or from the atom, _____ are formed. Adding electrons produces a _____

_____ whilst removing electrons produces a _____ _____ .

Insulators can become charged by _____ forces. _____ are transferred from one material to

another. When electrons are transferred from a material it becomes _____ _____ but when

electrons are transferred to a material it becomes _____ _____ .

Charged objects are surrounded by an _____ _____ which can be represented by a set of

_____ _____ _____ . These lines show the direction in which a force would act

on a small _____ charge placed in the field.

B Complete the diagrams below to show the lines of force acting around positively and negatively charged spheres.

$$+ \qquad -$$

C Explain how two objects can become charged when they are rubbed together.

HINT Your explanation should include the movement of charged particles. Which type of charged particle is free to move from one place to another?

_____

_____

_____

D Two oppositely charged objects are slowly brought together.

Describe the change in force between the two objects.

_____

_____

Explain why there may be a spark between the two objects when they get very close to each other.

_____

_____

_____

_____

P4.2 Current and charge

A Fill in the gaps to complete the sentences.

Every circuit component has its own circuit _____, and you use these to draw circuit diagrams.

A battery consists of two or more _____ .

Current is the _____ of flow of charge. You can calculate current using this equation, with units in the brackets:

$$\text{current (\_\_\_\_)} = \frac{\rule{4cm}{0.4pt}}{\rule{4cm}{0.4pt}}$$

[You need to remember this equation.]

B Next to each the name of each circuit component below, draw the circuit symbol.

diode		**resistor**	
fuse		**variable resistor**	
cell		**battery**	

C All of the following statements are false. Below each one write the correct statement.

a Charge is measured in amperes.

_____

_____

b Time is always measured in minutes.

_____

_____

c Current gets smaller further away from the battery.

_____

_____

d Current is the flow of charge.

_____

_____

D In a torch lamp, a charge of 15 C flows in 2 minutes. Calculate the current.

current = _____ A

P4.3 Potential difference and resistance

A Fill in the gaps to complete the sentences.

Potential difference is the _____ transferred to each charge by the battery, or the _____

transferred by each charge to the circuit component. Potential difference is measured in _____.

You can calculate potential difference and resistance using these equations:

$$\text{potential difference } (\underline{\hphantom{xx}}) = \frac{\overline{\hphantom{xxxxxxxxxxxxxx}}}{\underline{\hphantom{xxxxxxxxxxxxxx}}}$$

$$\text{resistance } (\underline{\hphantom{xx}}) = \frac{\overline{\hphantom{xxxxxxxxxxxxxx}}}{\underline{\hphantom{xxxxxxxxxxxxxx}}}$$

[You need to remember these equations.]

Ohm's law says that the current through a resistor is _____ _____ to the potential difference

across it. If you reverse the potential difference across a resistor, you _____ the current through it.

B a Sketch a circuit with a battery, lamp, ammeter, and voltmeter showing how to measure the current through the lamp and the potential difference across it.

b Explain the position of the ammeter and the voltmeter in the circuit.

_____

_____

c Suggest and explain what would happen to the readings on the ammeter if you reversed the battery.

_____

_____

C A charge flows through a resistor and transfers 200 J of energy. If the potential difference across it is 12 V, calculate the charge that flows through the resistor.

charge = _____ C

D a The resistor in activity **C** has a resistance of 30 Ω. Calculate the time it would take for 600 C to flow through it.

time = _____ s

b Give **one** assumption that you made about the resistor in part **a**.

_____

P4.4 Component characteristics

A Fill in the gaps to complete the sentences.

The resistance of a filament bulb _____ if the temperature increases.

For a diode the resistance in the forward direction is _____ and the resistance in the reverse direction is

_____ . A light-emitting diode (LED) emits light when a current passes through it in the _____

direction.

If the temperature of a thermistor increases, its resistance _____ . If the light intensity on a light-

dependent resistor (LDR) increases, its resistance _____ .

B Here are three graphs of current against potential difference (p.d.).

| Component **X** | Component **Y** | Component **Z** |

a Write the letter of the component that is an ohmic conductor, and explain your choice.

_____

_____

b Write the letter of the component that has a resistance that increases with p.d., and explain your choice.

_____

_____

c Name the remaining component, and describe how its resistance changes with p.d.

_____

_____

C Complete the table about light-dependent resistors and thermistors.

Device	Has a large resistance when it is ...	Has a small resistance when it is ...
light-dependent resistor		
thermistor		

D Explain why the resistance of a filament lamp increases with potential difference.

_____

_____

P4.5 Series circuits

A Fill in the gaps to complete the sentences.

In a series circuit:

- the _____ is the same in each component
- the total _____ _____ is shared between the components
- you find the total resistance by _____ the resistance of all the components.

If you have more than one cell in series, then you _____ all the potential differences to find the total potential difference.

If you add more resistors in series, the total resistance _____ . This is because the current through the resistors is _____ but the total potential difference across them is the same.

B Here is a series circuit.

a Complete the tables about the current and potential difference in the circuit. The bulbs are identical.

Position	Current in A
X	0.2
Y	
Z	

Component	Potential difference across it in V
cell	3
bulb 1	
bulb 2	

b Explain how you completed the tables.

_____

_____

_____

_____

C Calculate the resistance of each bulb in activity **B**, and the total resistance of the circuit.

resistance of each bulb = _____

total resistance of the circuit = _____

D A student removes a bulb from the circuit in activity **B**. Explain why this may not double the current in the circuit.

_____

_____

P4.6 Parallel circuits

A Fill in the gaps to complete the sentences.

In a parallel circuit:

● the _____ _____ across each component is the same

● you find the total _____ by adding the _____ through each component.

If you use a component that has a bigger resistance, the current through it will be _____ .

You can calculate current using this equation:

current (____) = ─────────────────────

[You need to remember this equation.]

If you add more resistors in parallel, the total resistance _____ because the total current _____ but the potential difference is the same.

B Here is a **parallel** circuit.

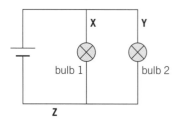

Position	Current in A
X	0.2
Y	
Z	

Component	Potential difference across it in V
cell	9
bulb 1	
bulb 2	

a Complete the tables about the current and potential difference in the circuit. The bulbs are identical.

b Explain how you completed the tables.

_____

_____

_____

_____

C Calculate the resistance of each bulb in activity **B**, and the total resistance of the circuit.

resistance of each bulb = _____

total resistance of the circuit = _____

D A student wants to increase the current through bulb 1 in the circuit in activity **B**. Describe **one** change she can make to the circuit to achieve this.

_____

P4 Practice questions

01 A student rubs two rods, made from different insulating materials, with a woollen cloth. When one rod is suspended as in **Figure 1** and the other rod is brought close to it, the suspended rod moves towards the other rod.

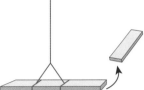

Figure 1

01.1 Write a conclusion that can be made about the charge on the two rods. [1 mark]

01.2 Explain why the rods need to be placed close together to detect this attraction effect. [2 marks]

02 A student is looking at two mystery circuits on the bench labelled circuit **A** and circuit **B**.
- Each circuit contains a battery pack, two bulbs, and two switches.
- All of the wires connecting the bulbs to the switches and battery have been covered up by black paper.
- The student knows that each switch is connected next to a bulb.
- All the bulbs are on.
- He knows that one of the circuits is wired in series and the other is wired in parallel.

02.1 Describe how the student can work out which circuit is in series and which is in parallel. [1 mark]

2.2 The resistance of one bulb is $10\,\Omega$, and the resistance of the other bulb is $15\,\Omega$. Calculate the resistance of the series circuit. [1 mark]

2.3 The p.d. of the battery in each circuit is 12V. Calculate the current through each bulb in the parallel circuit. [2 marks]

2.4 Calculate the total resistance of the parallel circuit. [3 marks]

03 A battery-operated fan spins when you turn it on.

03.1 A charge of 20C flows through the fan in 40 seconds. Show that the current is 0.5 A. [2 marks]

03.2 Write down Ohm's law. [2 marks]

03.3 The potential difference across the fan is 9V. Calculate the resistance. [2 marks]

03.4 Use the definitions of current and p.d. to explain why doubling the p.d. of the power supply to the fan multiplies the energy transferred to the fan per second by a factor of 4. [3 marks]

04 A student wants to monitor the light levels that a plant is receiving. She sets up the circuit in **Figure 2**.

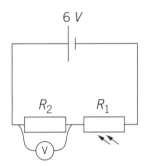

Figure 2

The resistance of the light-dependent resistor (LDR), R_1, is $100\,\Omega$ in the light and $500\,000\,\Omega$ in the dark. The resistance R_2 is $500\,\Omega$.

04.1 Explain why the light levels affect the reading on the voltmeter. [3 marks]

04.2 Calculate and compare the reading on the voltmeter when the LDR is in the light, and the dark. [6 marks]

P4 Checklist

	Student Book	☺	☺	☹
I can describe the structure of an atom, including the charges on the component particles.	4.1			
I can explain how materials become electrically charged by frictional forces.	4.1			
I can explain that the idea of an electric field gives rise to a non-contact force on a charged object.	4.1			
I can draw the shape of the electric field surrounding a charged sphere.	4.1			
I can describe how electric circuits are shown as diagrams.	4.2			
I can write down the difference between a battery and a cell.	4.2			
I can describe what determines the size of an electric current.	4.2			
I can calculate the size of an electric current from the charge flow and the time taken.	4.2			
I can write down what is meant by potential difference.	4.3			
I can write down what resistance is and what its unit is.	4.3			
I can write down Ohm's law.	4.3			
I can describe what happens when you reverse the potential difference across a resistor.	4.3			
I can describe what happens to the resistance of a filament lamp as its temperature increases.	4.4			
I can describe how the current through a diode depends on the potential difference across it.	4.4			
I can describe what happens to the resistance of a temperature-dependent resistor as its temperature increases.	4.4			
I can describe what happens to the resistance of a light-dependent resistor as the light level increases.	4.4			
I can describe the current, potential difference, and resistance for each component in a series circuit.	4.5			
I can describe the potential difference of several cells in series.	4.5			
I can calculate the total resistance of two resistors in series.	4.5			
I can explain why adding resistors in series increases the total resistance.	4.5			
I can describe the currents and potential differences for components in a parallel circuit.	4.6			
I can calculate the current through a resistor in a parallel circuit.	4.6			
I can explain why the total resistance of two resistors in parallel is less than the resistance of the smaller individual resistor.	4.6			
I can explain why adding resistors in parallel decreases the total resistance.	4.6			

P5.1 Alternating current

A Fill in the gaps to complete the sentences.

Direct current (d.c.) flows in _____ direction. Alternating current (a.c.) _____ its direction of flow.

In a mains circuit there is a live wire. Its potential difference alternates between _____ and

_____ every cycle. There is also a neutral wire. Its potential difference is _____ volts.

The National Grid is a _____ of cables and transformers that supply electricity to your home.

The peak potential difference of an a.c. supply is the _____ potential difference measured from

_____ volts. You can find the frequency of an a.c. supply by measuring the _____

_____, and using the equation:

$$\text{frequency } (\underline{\quad}) = \frac{\rule{6cm}{0.4pt}}{\rule{6cm}{0.4pt}}$$

B Compare a graph of potential difference against time for a d.c. circuit and for an a.c. circuit.

_____

_____

C Look at the graph.

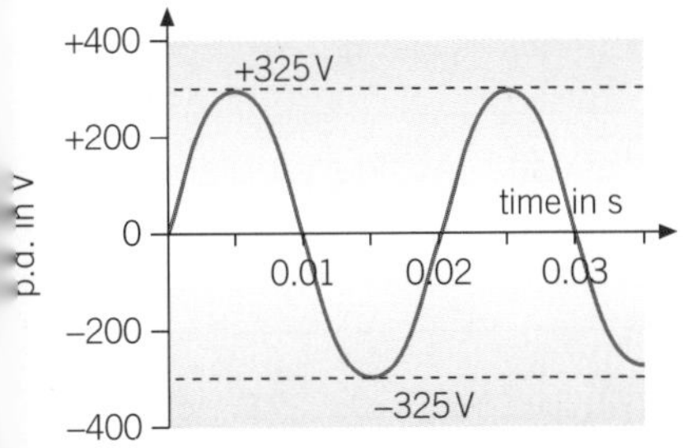

Write down the peak potential difference.

_____

Explain how to use the graph to find the frequency of the a.c.

_____

_____

Calculate the frequency of the p.d. shown on the graph.

_____

_____

Write down and explain whether the graph shows the p.d. of the live wire or the p.d. of the neutral wire.

_____

_____

Suggest why we say that mains voltage is 230 V, and not the peak voltage that is shown on the graph.

_____

P5.2 Cables and plugs

A Fill in the gaps to complete the sentences.

Sockets and plugs are made of stiff _____ that encloses electrical connections. This material is used because it is a good _____ .

A mains cable is made up of two or three insulated wires made of _____ surrounded by an outer layer of flexible _____ material.

In a three-pin plug or a three-core cable, the insulation on the live wire is coloured _____, the neutral wire is coloured _____, and the earth wire is coloured _____ and _____ .

The earth wire is connected to the _____ pin in a plug. It is used to earth the metal _____ of a mains appliance.

B a Complete the table showing the colours, functions, and potential differences of each of the wires in a mains cable.

Name of wire in a mains cable	Colour	Function	Potential difference in V
live		carries the current to make an appliance work	
	blue		
earth			0

  b Describe **one** similarity and **one** difference between the material insulating the wires inside a plug and the material of the plug casing.

  _____

  _____

C a Describe how you can get an electric shock from an appliance.

  _____

  _____

  b Explain how the fuse and earth wire protect you from an electric shock.

  _____

  _____

  _____

  c Suggest an appliance that does not need an earth wire. Explain your choice.

  _____

  _____

  d Suggest and explain what would happen if you connected an appliance using just the earth and neutral wires.

  _____

  _____

P5.3 Electrical power and potential difference

A Fill in the gaps to complete the sentences.

Power is the _____ transferred per second.

You can calculate energy transferred, the power, and the fuse rating using these equations:

energy transferred (_____) = _____

electrical power (_____) = _____

fuse rating (_____) = $\dfrac{\rule{200pt}{0.5pt}}{\rule{200pt}{0.5pt}}$

[You need to remember these equations.]

B a Define power.

_____

_____

b All mains appliances use the same potential difference.

Describe and explain the link between the power rating of an appliance and the fuse rating it needs.

_____

_____

_____

C An electric car has an electric motor with a power of 15 kW.

Calculate the energy transferred during a 2 ½ hour car journey.

energy transferred = _____ J

D a Calculate the current in a mains (230 V) microwave that has a power of 1000 W.

current = _____ A

b The fuses available are 1 A, 3 A, 5 A, and 13 A. Write down the fuse that you need for the microwave oven in part **a**. Explain your choice.

_____

_____

Calculate the resistance of a mains (230 V) games console. It needs a current of 1.5 A. It has a power of 350 W.

resistance = _____ Ω

A Fill in the gaps to complete the sentences.

You can calculate charge flow and the energy transferred using these equations, with units in the brackets:

charge (_____) = _____

energy (_____) = _____

[You need to remember these equations.]

When charge flows through a resistor, the energy transferred makes the resistor _____ .

When charge flows around a circuit, the _____ supplied by the battery is equal to

the _____ transferred to all the components in the circuit.

B Use the idea of electrons to explain why a wire gets hot when a current flows.

_____

_____

_____

C a You might sometimes have felt a small shock from a car door handle. When this happens a current of about 4 mA flows for about 0.1 s.

Calculate the charge that flows.

charge = _____ C

b When you use a toaster, the wire inside the toaster heats up. The toaster is connected to the mains at 230 V, and a charge of 300 000 C flows.

Calculate the energy transferred.

energy transferred = _____ J

D A student calculates the energy transferred to the components in a circuit as 120 J, and the energy transferred by the battery as 125 J.

Explain why these two values are not exactly equal.

_____

_____

_____

_____

P5.5 Appliances and efficiency

A Fill in the gaps to complete the sentences.

A domestic meter measures how much _____ is transferred by appliances in your home.

You can calculate energy supplied to an appliance, or the useful energy, using the equations:

Energy supplied (_____) = _____

Useful energy (_____) = _____

Useful power (_____) = _____

[Include units. You need to be able to remember these equations.]

B Jules uses an electric oven to cook a chicken. The oven needs a potential difference of 230 V and has a current flowing through it of 15 A.

a Calculate the power of the oven. Write your answer to an appropriate number of significant figures.

power = _____ W

b Jules now wants to calculate the energy transferred to the oven.

Name the other quantity that he will need. _____

C a It takes 30 minutes to cook a pizza in an oven with a power of 2000 W.

Calculate the energy transferred.

energy transferred = _____ J

b Another oven is 70% efficient. It supplies 4000 kJ.

Calculate the useful energy.

useful energy = _____ J

c Both ovens supply the same amount of useful energy. Calculate the efficiency of the oven in part **a**.

efficiency = _____ %

P5 Practice questions

01 **Table 1** shows some information about three wires in a plug.

Table 1

Wire	Colour	Statement
A		connected to the metal casing of an appliance
B		at 230 V
C		at 0 V

01.1 Complete the table by writing the colour of each wire. [2 marks]

01.2 Write down the letter of the earth wire.

_____ [1 mark]

01.3 Write down the letters of the **two** wires that make a complete circuit with an appliance.

_____ [1 mark]

01.4 Write down the name of the network of wires and transformers to which the plug is connected.

_____ [1 mark]

02 Complete **Table 2** by writing down for each material the part of a plug it is used for and why.

Table 2 [3 marks]

Material	The part of a plug it is used for	Reason
hard plastic		
flexible plastic		
copper		

03 A student has some hair straighteners. The label says: 1100 W, 230 V. Calculate the fuse that she needs to use in the plug. The fuses available are 3 A, 5 A, and 13 A. [4 marks]

_____

_____

04 A student does a survey of the appliances in her kitchen. **Table 3** shows the results. All the appliances work on a potential difference of 230 V (the mains).

Table 3

Appliance	Power rating in W	Current in A
kettle	1200	5.2
microwave	800	3.5
refrigerator	420	1.8

04.1 Calculate the energy transferred when you microwave popcorn for 2 minutes. [3 marks]

_____

_____

04.2 Calculate the charge that flows through a kettle during the 6 minutes that it takes to boil. [3 marks]

_____

_____

04.3 The refrigerator is on all day and all night. Calculate the energy transferred in one day. [3 marks]

_____

_____

05 A student uses an oscilloscope to displace a low-voltage alternating p.d. The screen is shown in **Figure 1**.

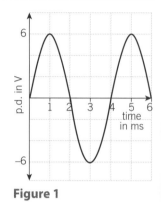

Figure 1

05.1 Calculate the frequency of the p.d. [4 marks]

_____

_____

05.2 Give **two** features of the graph that tell you it is not showing mains electricity. [2 marks]

_____

_____

06 The graph in **Figure 2** shows how the efficiency of two types of washer has changed over time.

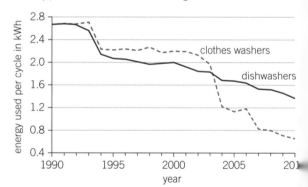

Figure 2

The energy needed to clean a load in a dishwasher is 3 MJ. Compare the energy wasted by a typical dishwasher in 1990 with that of a typical dishwasher in 2010. [6 marks]

_____

_____

_____

_____

_____

_____

P5 Checklist

	Student Book	☺	😐	☹
I can write down what direct current is and what alternating current is.	5.1			
I can describe what is meant by the live wire and the neutral wire of a mains circuit.	5.1			
I can describe the National Grid.	5.1			
I can describe how to use an oscilloscope to measure the frequency and peak potential difference of an alternating current.	5.1			
I can describe what the casing of a mains plug or socket is made of and explain why.	5.2			
I can write down what is in a mains cable.	5.2			
I can write down the colours of the live, neutral, and earth wires.	5.2			
I can explain why a three-pin plug includes an earth pin.	5.2			
I can describe how power and energy are related.	5.3			
I can use the power rating of an appliance to calculate the energy transferred in a given time.	5.3			
I can calculate the electrical power supplied to a device from its current and potential difference.	5.3			
I can work out the correct fuse to use in an appliance.	5.3			
I can calculate the flow of electric charge given the current and time.	5.4			
I can write down the energy transfers when electric charge flows through a resistor.	5.4			
I can describe how the energy transferred by a flow of electric charge is related to potential difference.	5.4			
I can link the electrical energy supplied by the battery in a circuit to the energy transferred to the electrical components.	5.4			
I can calculate the energy supplied to an electrical appliance from its current, its potential difference, and how long it is used for.	5.5			
I can work out the useful energy output of an electrical appliance.	5.5			
I can work out the output power of an electrical appliance.	5.5			
I can compare different appliances that do the same job.	5.5			

P6.1 Density

A Fill in the gaps to complete the sentences.

Density depends on _____ and _____, and is measured in _____.

You can calculate density using the equation:

$$\text{density} (\_\_\_\_\_) = \frac{\underline{\hspace{4cm}}}{\underline{\hspace{4cm}}}$$

[Include units. You need to be able to remember this equation]

From this you can work out that mass = _____ × _____, and volume = $\frac{\underline{\hspace{2cm}}}{\underline{\hspace{2cm}}}$.

You use a digital balance to measure _____, and a ruler or measuring cylinder to measure

_____.

An object will float on water if its density is _____ _____ that of water.

B Calculate the **density** of a person with a mass of 55.0 kg and a volume of 0.0700 m³.

density = _____ kg/m³

C A ship is much heavier than a small pebble. But whilst the ship can float on water, a pebble sinks. Explain why.

_____

_____

_____

_____

D Compare how you would find the density of a stone cube and how you would find the density of an irregular piece of modelling clay.

_____

_____

_____

_____

E Material **X** has a density of 1.5 g/cm³. Material **Y** has a density of 5 g/cm³. A block of material **Y** has the same mass as 10 cm³ of material **X**.

Calculate the volume of the block of material **Y**.

_____

P6.2 States of matter

A Fill in the gaps to complete the sentences.

In a _____ the particles move about randomly and are far apart. In a _____ the particles move at random and are in contact with each other. In a _____ the particles are held next to each other in fixed positions.

A _____ is the least energetic state of matter, and a _____ is the most energetic state of matter.

When a substance changes state, the _____ stays the same because the number of particles stays the same.

B Use the particle arrangements of solids and liquids to explain why the densities of a solid and liquid metal are similar.

_____

_____

_____

C **a** Label each of the arrows in the diagram with the correct name of the change of state.

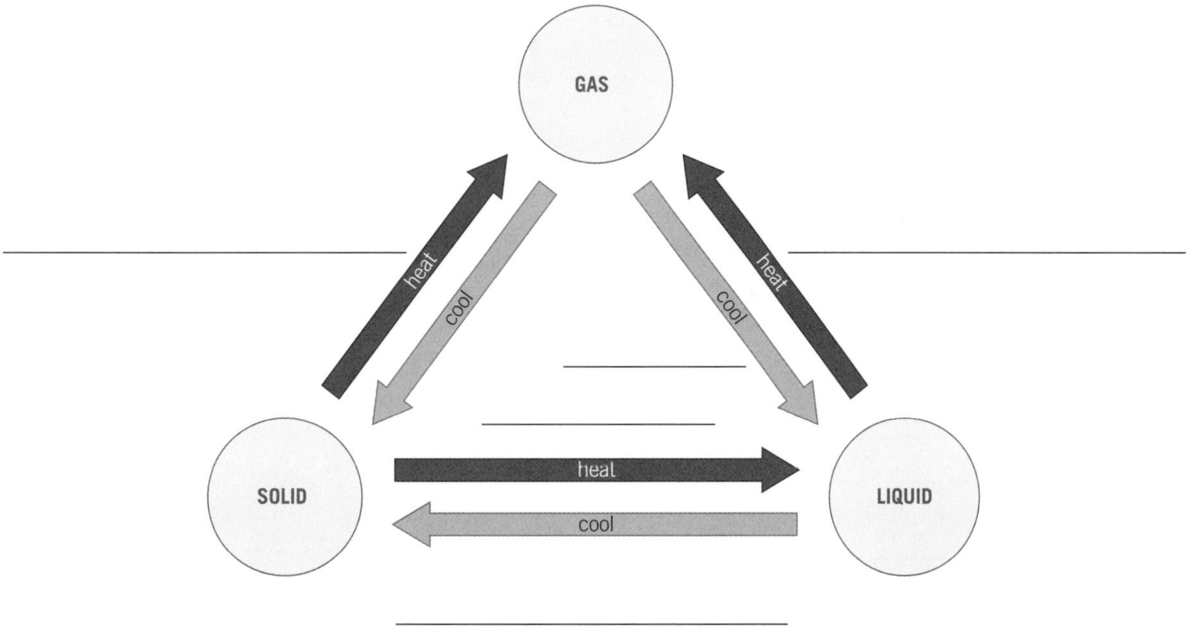

b Explain why liquid is a more energetic state than a solid.

_____

_____

⊃ The water in a cat's bowl evaporates over time.

Write down what happens to the number of molecules of water in the bowl over time.

_____

Explain how mass is conserved in this situation.

_____

_____

Explain why this is a **physical change**.

_____

P6.3 Changes of state

A Fill in the gaps to complete the sentences.

The melting point of a pure substance is the temperature at which it _____ or _____ , and the boiling

point is the temperature at which it _____ or _____ .

You can find the melting point or boiling point from the _____ section of a temperature–time graph.

_____ occurs throughout a liquid at its boiling point, but _____ occurs from the surface of a liquid at a
temperature below its boiling point.

B Tick the boxes to show whether each statement is true for boiling or evaporation. You may need to tick **both**
boxes for some statements.

Statement	✓ if true for boiling	✓ if true for evaporation
This process happens at the **boiling point** of the liquid.		
The mass does not change.		
The particles escape only from the surface of the liquid.		
This process happens at or below the boiling point of the liquid.		

C Jo took some ice out of the freezer and put it on a plate in a warm room. This graph shows what happened to the
temperature of the ice over time.

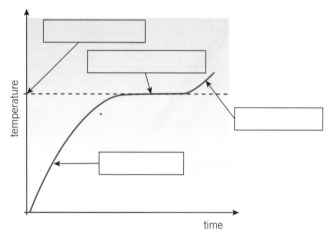

a Label the diagram using the words below.

melting point   **liquid**   **solid + liquid**   **solid**

b Jo then reversed the process by putting the melted ice back in
the freezer.

Sketch a graph of temperature against time for this process.

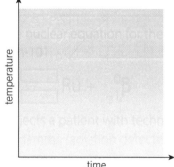

c Suggest **one** change you would need to make when labelling this graph compared with the graph in
activity **C**.

_____

P6.4 Internal energy

A Fill in the gaps to complete the sentences.

If the temperature of a substance increases, its internal energy _____ .

The strength of the forces of _____ between the particles explains why a substance is a solid, liquid, or gas.

If you heat a substance and its temperature rises, the _____ energy of its particles increases. If you heat a substance and its temperature *does not* rise, the _____ energy of its particles increases.

The pressure of a gas on a surface is caused by the particles of the gas repeatedly _____ the surface.

B Tick **all** the descriptions of energy that apply to the **internal energy** of a substance in different states.

Energy	✓ if included in internal energy
the kinetic energy of the particles in a gas	
the energy of vibration of the particles in a solid	
the gravitational potential energy of the particles in a liquid	
the kinetic energy of a whole solid	

C Write a sentence to explain why a gas exerts a pressure on the surfaces that enclose it.

_____

_____

D **a** Compare a liquid getting hotter and a solid cooling down. Use the idea of changes in the potential energy and kinetic energy of particles.

_____

_____

_____

b Explain why you can heat a substance but not observe a temperature rise. Use the ideas of internal, kinetic, and potential energy.

_____

_____

_____

_____

_____

P6.5 Specific latent heat

A Fill in the gaps to complete the sentences.

Latent heat is the _____ you need to transfer to a substance to change its state without changing its

_____ .

Specific latent heat of fusion or vaporisation is the energy you need to transfer to a substance to melt or boil a mass of

_____ of the substance without changing its _____ .

You can calculate the energy transferred using this equation, with units in the brackets:

thermal energy for a change of state (_____) = _____

You can measure the specific latent heat of ice or water using a low-voltage heater to _____ the ice, or

to _____ the water.

B Compare latent heat and specific latent heat, using their definitions and units.

_____

_____

_____

C A student wanted to measure the thermal energy needed to melt ice. He measured the mass of some ice. He melted the ice and measured the mass of the water. The **specific latent heat of fusion** of ice is 334 kJ/kg, and the mass of water melted was 0.03 kg.

Calculate the thermal energy for this change of state. Give your answer to an appropriate number of significant figures.

thermal energy for melting ice = _____ J

D For a given substance, the specific latent heat of vaporisation is higher than the specific latent heat of fusion. Explain why. Use the ideas of potential energy, kinetic energy, and bonds.

_____

_____

_____

_____

_____

_____

P6.6 Gas pressure and temperature

A Fill in the gaps to complete the sentences.

Gas molecules colliding with the surfaces in contact with the gas cause gas _____ .

If the temperature of a gas in a sealed container increases, the pressure _____ because:

- there are _____ impacts per second
- the force of the impacts _____ .

You can see evidence for the _____ motion of gas molecules by observing smoke particles.

B Write a sentence to describe a piece of evidence for the motion of gas molecules.

_____

_____

_____

_____

C The pressure of a gas increases as it is heated. Explain why, by describing its particles.

_____

_____

D Molly carried out an investigation into the relationship between temperature and pressure. Here is the graph that she plotted from her results.

Describe **two** variables that Molly needs to keep constant.
Explain why.

_____

_____

_____

_____

Molly heats the gas in a steel container. As the temperature increases, the seal of the container leaks.
Suggest what this would do to Molly's graph.

_____

_____

_____

_____

P6.7 Gas pressure and volume

A Fill in the gaps to complete the sentences.

The volume of a fixed mass of gas depends on its _____ and its _____.

Imagine a gas contained in a cylinder with a piston at one end, so that the volume occupied by the gas can change.

If the gas is slowly _____ by the piston moving inwards, the gas pressure will increase. If the gas is

allowed to _____, the pressure will decrease.

For a fixed mass of gas, _____ × _____ = constant, as long at the _____ is kept

constant. This relationship is known as _____ _____.

When the gas is compressed by exerting a force on the piston, _____ is done on the gas. If this happens

quickly, the _____ of the gas will increase.

B When the volume of a cylinder of gas is reduced, the gas pressure increases.

Explain the cause of this pressure increase in terms of particle behaviour.

_____

_____

_____

_____

_____

C Complete the table to show the changes in pressure or volume for three gases at different temperatures.

Initial pressure in Pa	Initial volume in m³	Final pressure in Pa	Final volume in m³
80 000	0.20	40 000	a
200 000	1.40	b	4.20
75 000	c	375 000	0.025

D a Explain why the air inside a bicycle pump increases in temperature when the pump is used to inflate a tyre quickly.

_____

_____

_____

_____

b An aerosol used for cleaning computer keyboards contains compressed air.

Suggest why the can becomes colder if the gas is allowed to escape rapidly.

_____

_____

_____

_____

P6 Practice questions

01 Write the definition of latent heat. [1 mark]
_____
_____

02 Compare each of the following changes of state, in terms of particles.

02.1 Freezing and melting. [2 marks]
_____
_____

02.2 Evaporation and boiling. [2 marks]
_____
_____

03 Gas is contained inside a weather balloon which has a volume of 4.00 m³ when at ground level where the air pressure is 100 kPa. The balloon is released and rises slowly upwards through the atmosphere.

03.1 Describe what will happen to the volume of the balloon as it rises. [1 mark]
_____
_____

03.2 Calculate the volume of the balloon when it reaches a height where the air pressure is 75 kPa. [2 marks]
_____
_____

03.3 Give **one** assumption made during the calculation in question **03.2**. [1 mark]
_____
_____

04 **Figure 1** shows a graph of the temperature of a liquid as it is heated.

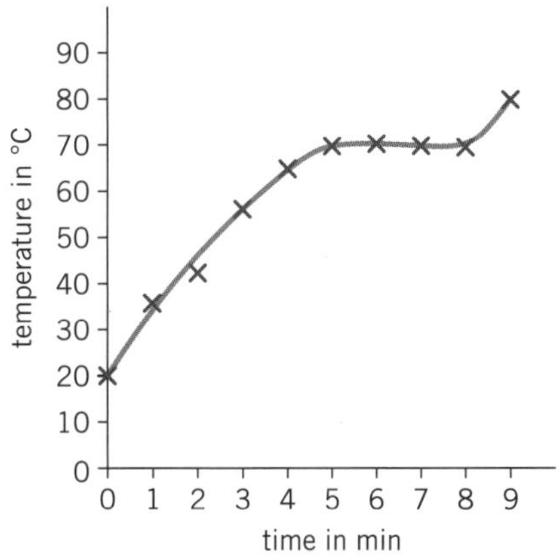

Figure 1

4.1 Write down the boiling point of the liquid.
_____ [1 mark]

4.2 Write down the time when the particles have the least potential energy. _____ [1 mark]

04.3 Write down the time when the particles have the least kinetic energy. _____ [1 mark]

04.4 Describe what happens to the internal energy of the liquid between 5 and 8 minutes. [2 marks]
_____
_____

05.1 Sort these steps into the correct order to describe how to measure the specific latent heat of fusion of ice. Write the letters in order below. [4 marks]

A Look at the joulemeter to record the energy transferred by the heater during the 10 minutes.

B Turn the heater on.

C Allow the ice to melt for 10 minutes and measure the mass of water collected.

D Put ice in a funnel, put the funnel in a beaker on a digital balance, and put a heater into the ice, but do not turn it on.

E Use the equation specific latent heat = energy/mass of water collected, to find the specific latent heat.

Correct order: _____
_____

05.2 Suggest and explain why a student using this method might observe a value for the latent heat of fusion that is higher than the accepted value. [3 marks]
_____
_____
_____
_____

06 An ice cube of mass 2 g melts, and the water heats up to room temperature, which is 20 °C.
The specific latent heat of melting of ice is 334 000 J/kg, and the specific heat capacity of water is 4200 J/kg °C.
Calculate the total energy supplied to the ice cube.
Use these equations:
thermal energy for a change of state = mass × specific latent heat
change in thermal energy = mass × specific heat capacity × temperature change [4 marks]
_____
_____
_____
_____
_____
_____
_____
_____
_____

P6 Checklist

	Student Book	☺	☺	☹
I can define density and write down its unit.	6.1			
I can describe how to measure the density of a solid object or a liquid.	6.1			
I can use the density equation to calculate the mass or the volume of an object or a sample.	6.1			
I can describe how to tell from its density if an object will float in water.	6.1			
I can describe the different properties of solids, liquids, and gases.	6.2			
I can describe the arrangement of particles in a solid, a liquid, and a gas.	6.2			
I can explain why gases are less dense than solids and liquids.	6.2			
I can explain why the mass of a substance that changes state stays the same.	6.2			
I can write down what the melting point and the boiling point of a substance mean.	6.3			
I can describe what you need to do to melt a solid or to boil a liquid.	6.3			
I can explain the difference between boiling and evaporation.	6.3			
I can use a temperature–time graph to find the melting point or the boiling point of a substance.	6.3			
I can describe how increasing the temperature of a substance affects its internal energy.	6.4			
I can explain the different properties of a solid, a liquid, and a gas.	6.4			
I can describe how the energy of the particles of a substance changes when it is heated.	6.4			
I can explain in terms of particles why a gas exerts pressure.	6.4			
I can write down what latent heat means as a substance changes its state.	6.5			
I can write down what specific latent heat of fusion and of vaporisation mean.	6.5			
I can use specific latent heat in calculations.	6.5			
I can describe how to measure the specific latent heat of ice and of water.	6.5			
I can describe how a gas exerts pressure on a surface.	6.6			
I can describe how changing the temperature of a gas in a sealed container affects the pressure of the gas.	6.6			
I can explain why raising the temperature of a gas in a sealed container increases the pressure of the gas.	6.6			
I can describe how to see evidence of gas molecules moving around at random.	6.6			
I can describe why the temperature of a gas can increase when it is compressed quickly.	6.7			
I can explain why the pressure of a gas in a container increases when it is compressed.	6.7			
I can use Boyle's law to find changes in the pressure and volume of a gas.	6.7			
I can explain why the temperature of a gas increases if it is compressed quickly.	6.7			

P7.1 Atoms and radiation

A Fill in the gaps to complete the sentences.

A radioactive substance contains _____ nuclei that usually become _____ after emitting radiation.

Radioactive sources emit three main types of radiation: _____ , _____ , and

_____ .

You cannot predict when a nucleus will emit radiation, so we say radioactive decay is _____ .

B Give an example, apart from radioactive decay, of a random process, and explain why it is random.

_____

_____

C Complete the table by writing the missing types of radiation, the symbol for each type, and the part of the atom that emits the radiation. You may need to use the same word more than once.

Type of radiation	Symbol	Part of the atom that emits the radiation
alpha		
	γ	
	β	

D A scientist is investigating a radioactive rock specimen using a Geiger counter. There is a reading on the counter that shows the number of counts per second.

Describe what is causing the reading to change.

_____

_____

Describe and explain how the scientist could work out whether the specimen is emitting alpha radiation.

_____

_____

_____

Explain in terms of atoms why the Geiger counter produces a reading with some rocks but not others.

_____

_____

_____

P7.2 The discovery of the nucleus

A Fill in the gaps to complete the sentences.

Rutherford used _____ particles to probe atoms. He fired them at a thin metal foil and discovered

that most of them went through, but some were scattered by _____ angles.

He could not explain this scattering using the _____ _____ model.

Rutherford's model said that most of the mass of the atom is in a _____ ,

_____ charged nucleus in the centre of an atom.

B Look at the diagram of Rutherford's experiment with alpha particles.

fixed thin metal foil

θ

α source in a lead box
with a narrow hole

evacuated
chamber

incident α
particles

atoms in the
metal foil

nucleus

a In the right-hand diagram, two of the alpha particles are scattered back in the direction that they came from.
Draw the paths of those two alpha particles.

b Describe and explain the link between the number of alpha particles scattered backwards and Rutherford's model
of the atom.

_____

_____

_____

C Compare Rutherford's model of the atom with Bohr's model of the atom.

_____

_____

_____

_____

_____

_____

P7.3 Changes in the nucleus

A Fill in the gaps to complete the sentences.

Isotopes of an element are atoms with the _____ number of protons but a

_____ number of neutrons. They have the _____ atomic number but

_____ mass numbers.

When a nucleus emits an alpha particle it loses _____ protons and _____

neutrons. The mass number goes down by _____, and the atomic number goes down by

_____ .

When a nucleus emits a beta particle a _____ changes to a _____ and

emits an _____ . The mass number _____ _____

_____, and the atomic number goes up by _____ .

B a Here are some symbols for atoms. The names of the elements have been replaced with an 'X'.

Circle the **two** isotopes of the same element.

$$^{14}_{6}X \qquad ^{14}_{7}X \qquad ^{12}_{6}X$$

b Explain the decision you made in part **a**.

_____

_____

C Compare alpha decay and beta decay by describing the changes in the nucleus.

_____

_____

_____

_____

D Use the periodic table to write balanced equations for the decay of the following isotopes by alpha and beta decay.

The alpha decay of $^{226}_{88}Ra$: $^{226}_{88}Ra \rightarrow$ _____ + _____

The beta decay of $^{218}_{84}Po$: $^{218}_{84}Po \rightarrow$ _____ + _____

E Compare γ emission and neutron emission.

_____

_____

_____

_____

_____

_____

A Fill in the gaps to complete the sentences.

Alpha radiation is stopped by _____, beta radiation is stopped by _____, and the intensity of gamma radiation is reduced by _____.

In air, alpha radiation has a range of ___ ___ ____, beta radiation has a range of ____ _____, and gamma radiation has an _____ range.

An alpha particle consists of _____ protons and _____ neutrons, a beta particle is a _____-moving _____, and gamma radiation is _____ radiation.

Alpha radiation is the _____ ionising, and gamma radiation is the _____ ionising.

All three types of radiation _____ substances as they pass through them, which can _____ or kill living cells.

B A student has a sample that is radioactive. She wants to identify the type or types of radiation emitted by the sample.

Describe and explain how the student can use a Geiger counter and samples of different materials to identify the emitted radiation.

_____

_____

_____

_____

C a In the table, write the correct type of radiation (α, β, γ) next to each description.

it has an infinite range in air		it consists of a fast moving electron	
it is moderately ionising		it is the most ionising	
it has a range of about 1 m in air		it has a range of a few cm in air	
it consists of two protons and two neutrons		it consists of electromagnetic radiation	

b One description is missing. Write the description and the type of radiation here:

_____

D A friend finds out that a pack of strawberries has been irradiated. He thinks that eating them will give him cancer.

Suggest what you can say to reassure him.

_____

_____

_____

_____

P7.5 Activity and half-life

A Fill in the gaps to complete the sentences.

The half-life of a radioactive isotope is the average time it takes for the number of nuclei of the isotope to

_____ .

The count rate of a Geiger counter decreases as the activity of a radioactive source _____ .

In one half-life the activity and the number of atoms of a radioactive isotope will _____ .

You can find the count rate of a radioactive isotope after n half-lives by dividing the initial count rate by

_____ .

B Explain the difference between **count rate** and **activity**.

_____

_____

C Tick **all** of the correct definitions of **half-life**.

Definition	✓ if correct
Half-life is the time for the number of alpha particles to halve.	
Half-life is the time for the number of unstable nuclei to halve.	
Half-life is the time for the activity to halve.	
Half-life is the time for the amount of radiation to halve.	

D Look at the graph. It shows the decay of radioactive iodine.

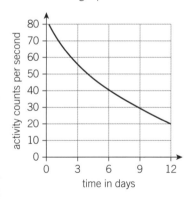

Write down the half-life of the iodine. _____

Calculate the activity after three half-lives.

_____

_____

Calculate the time when the activity becomes five counts per second. Show how you calculated the time.

_____

_____

Calculate the ratio of net decline of the iodine after six half-lives.

_____

_____

P7.6 Nuclear radiation in medicine

A Fill in the gaps to complete the sentences.

Nuclear radiation can be used to _____ and treat medical disorders.

A _____ _____ can be used to trace the flow of a substance through an organ to discover

if that organ is functioning correctly. These tracers emit _____ radiation which can be detected outside

the body by a _____ _____. Tracers should have a _____ half-life so that they

do not remain in the body for a long period of time before decaying into a _____ _____.

The medical procedure of _____ uses a powerful gamma source to produce a _____

_____ of radiation which is directed at tumours to destroy their cells. Tumours can also be treated by

embedding small _____ sources inside the body that emit radiation to destroy cancer cells.

B Describe measures taken to protect medical personnel who work with radioactive materials.

_____

_____

_____

C Write down **three** natural sources of background radiation.

_____

_____

D The two charts below show the intensity of gamma radiation emitted by a healthy kidney (**A**) and a kidney with a blockage (**B**) after a radioactive tracer has been injected.

a chart recorder **A**

b chart recorder **B**

a Describe how the charts show that there is a blockage in kidney **B**.

HINT Think about why the count rate goes up and what should happen if the kidney is healthy.

_____

_____

_____

b Explain why a radioactive tracer with a half-life of five minutes would be unsuitable for use as a tracer in this procedure.

_____

_____

_____

P7.7 Nuclear fission

A Fill in the gaps to complete the sentences.

Nuclear fission occurs when an unstable _____ absorbs a _____ and splits into two smaller

parts. This process releases energy in the form of _____ _____ and _____ ,

which can go on to split more and more nuclei in a _____ _____ .

In a nuclear reactor, the fissionable isotopes are in the _____ _____ . A _____ ,

such as water, is used to slow down emitted neutrons so that they are moving at the correct speed to cause more

fission reactions. The rate of the chain reaction is kept constant by _____ _____ which

_____ some of the released neutrons, so that each fission neutron causes one more fission.

B The diagram shows a simplified nuclear fission reactor.

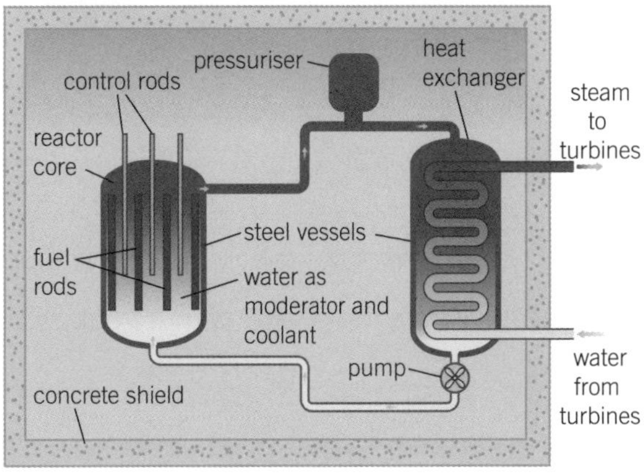

a Describe the purpose of the following parts of the reactor.

control rods _____

_____

fuel rods _____

_____

moderator _____

_____

coolant _____

_____

b Give reasons why the reactor is contained within a thick steel shell and a concrete shield.

_____

_____

C A nuclear reactor uses a 'controlled chain reaction' to heat the coolant.

Explain what is meant by a chain reaction.

_____

_____

_____

_____

In a nuclear reactor the chain reaction is kept at a constant 'critical' level.

Explain what would happen if the reaction were not controlled.

_____

_____

_____

P7.8 Nuclear fusion

A Fill in the gaps to complete the sentences.

Nuclear fusion is the process where two _____ _____ are fused together to form a

_____ nucleus; this process releases energy.

Nuclear fusion is the reaction that takes place in the core of the _____ and other _____,
causing heating.

B The diagram below shows a series of fusion reactions that happen in the Sun and produce helium nuclei.

● proton
○ neutron

a This series of reactions releases a large amount of energy in the form of radiation.

Describe where this energy comes from.

_____

_____

b Complete this nuclear equation which represents one of the reactions shown in the diagram.

$$^3_2\text{He} + \underline{}\text{He} \rightarrow \underline{}\text{He} + \underline{}\text{p}$$

C a Complete the table to identify the advantages and disadvantages of nuclear fusion when compared to
nuclear fission.

Advantages of nuclear fusion	Disadvantages of nuclear fusion

b Give the main reason why no functioning commercial nuclear fusion reactors have been built.

_____

_____

P7.9 Nuclear issues

A Fill in the gaps to complete the sentences.

Radioactive substances exist naturally all around us and produce a level of _____ _____.

Most of this natural radiation is produced by a gas called _____. This gas is particularly dangerous

because it is breathed into the lungs where the _____ _____ it emits are very harmful.

The processing of used fuel rods from nuclear fission reactors produces _____ _____, some

of which is highly active. Some of it has a very long _____ – _____ and needs to be stored

for hundreds, or even thousands, of years until its _____ has reduced to safer levels.

Nuclear accidents at reactors such as those at _____ and Fukushima can release _____

_____ into the atmosphere. These substances are very dangerous and large areas of land need to be

evacuated for long periods of time.

B Name **three** non-natural sources of background radiation and suggest how your exposure to them could be reduced.

_____

_____

_____

_____

_____

_____

C Alpha, beta, and gamma radiation all cause damage to cells but their degree of danger varies in different situations.

Complete this table to describe the relative risks of the three sources inside and outside the body.

		Alpha particles	Beta particles	Gamma rays
Inside body	**Level of danger**	very high	high	medium
	Explanation	a	b	cause lower levels of ionisation (than alpha and beta) and so less damage to cells
Outside body	**Level of danger**	fairly low	c	d
	Explanation	cannot penetrate the skin and so cannot damage internal organs	e	f

P7 Practice questions

01 A radioactive sample emits alpha, beta, and gamma radiation.

01.1 Compare these three types of radiation, by describing the types of particle or wave, types of absorber, and ranges in air. [3 marks]

_____

_____

_____

_____

01.2 Explain the link between the ionising power of the different types of radiation and their range in air. [3 marks]

_____

_____

02 Nuclear fission reactors are used to generate approximately 20% of the UK's electricity.

Describe how the reactor core operates to generate high pressure steam in a nuclear fission reactor. [6 marks]

_____

_____

_____

_____

_____

_____

_____

_____

_____

03 Here are some statements about what happens to the atomic mass and atomic number of a nucleus that decays.
Write a possible type of decay (α, β, γ) for each statement.

03.1 The mass number goes down by four. [1 mark]

_____

03.2 The atomic number does not change. [1 mark]

_____

03.3 The atomic number goes up by one. [1 mark]

_____

03.4 The mass number does not change. [1 mark]

_____

04 **Figure 1** is a graph of the activity of a radioactive sample of californium against time.

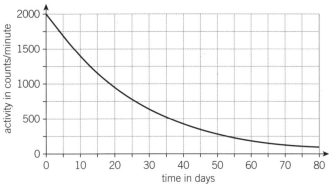

Figure 1

04.1 The activity of californium halves every 18 days. Write down, in terms of nuclei, what else halves in18 days. [1 mark]

_____

_____

04.2 Calculate the activity of californium after five half-lives. [4 marks]

_____

_____

_____

05 A radiographer in a hospital is preparing a sample of technetium-99. She shields herself from the radiation that the technetium emits.

05.1 Explain why radiation is hazardous to the human body. [1 mark]

_____

_____

05.2 A different isotope of technetium, technetium-101 has a half-life of 15 minutes and emits beta radiation. Describe the difference between a nucleus of technetium-99 and a nucleus of technetium-101. [2 marks]

_____

_____

05.3 Complete the nuclear equation for the beta decay of technetium-101. [2 marks]

$$^{101}_{43}\text{Tc} \rightarrow \boxed{}\atop\boxed{}\text{Ru} + ^{0}_{-1}\beta$$

05.4 The doctor injects a patient with technetium-99. She uses the gamma radiation detected with a special camera to diagnose kidney problems in the patient. Explain why the doctor does not use technetium-101 for this procedure. [3 marks]

_____

_____

P7 Checklist

	Student Book	☺	☺	☹
I can write down what a radioactive substance is.	7.1			
I can write down the types of radiation given out from a radioactive substance.	7.1			
I can write down what happens when a radioactive source emits radiation (radioactive decay).	7.1			
I can write down the different types of radiation emitted by radioactive sources.	7.1			
I can describe how the nuclear model of the atom was established.	7.2			
I can explain why the 'plum pudding' model of the atom was rejected.	7.2			
I can describe what conclusions were made about the atom from experimental evidence.	7.2			
I can explain why the nuclear model was accepted.	7.2			
I can write down what an isotope is.	7.3			
I can describe how the nucleus of an atom changes when it emits an alpha particle or a beta particle.	7.3			
I can represent the emission of an alpha particle from a nucleus.	7.3			
I can represent the emission of a beta particle from a nucleus.	7.3			
I can write down how far each type of radiation can travel in air.	7.4			
I can describe how different materials absorb alpha, beta, and gamma radiation.	7.4			
I can describe the ionising power of alpha, beta, and gamma radiation.	7.4			
I can explain why alpha, beta, and gamma radiation are dangerous.	7.4			
I can write down what the half-life of a radioactive source means.	7.5			
I can write down what the count rate from a radioactive source means.	7.5			
I can describe what happens to the count rate from a radioactive isotope as it decays.	7.5			
I can write down what the count rate from a radioactive source means.	7.5			
I can calculate the count rate after a given number of half-lives.	7.5			
I can calculate the count rate after a given number of half-lives.	7.5			
can describe how medical tracers can be used to diagnose conditions.	7.6			
can describe how radioactive substances can be used to treat medical conditions.	7.6			
can describe the process of nuclear fission including the behaviour of the particles involved.	7.7			
can explain how a chain reaction can occur during nuclear fission.	7.7			
can describe the operation of a nuclear fission reactor including the function of fuel ods, control rods, a moderator and a coolant.	7.7			
can describe the process of nuclear fusion between light nuclei.	7.8			
can explain a range of issues related to the use of nuclear power.	7.9			

P8.1 Vectors and scalars

A Fill in the gaps to complete the sentences.

Displacement is the _____ in a given direction.

A vector quantity is a physical quantity that has _____ and _____ . A scalar quantity is a physical quantity that has _____ only.

You can represent a vector quantity with an arrow. The direction of the arrow tells you the _____ of the vector, and the length of the arrow tells you the _____ of the vector.

B a Write down a scalar quantity that you have measured in an experiment, and explain why it is not a vector.

_____

_____

b Explain why vectors are shown by arrows.

_____

C A tortoise walks 20 cm west, then 30 cm north, and then 40 cm east. You may want to draw a diagram to help your calculations.

Calculate:

a the final displacement of the tortoise

_____

b the total distance that the tortoise travels.

_____

D A toy boat is travelling north across a lake. The driving force of the engine on the boat is 20 N. The force of the wind on the boat is 5 N west. The wind is blowing at 90° to the direction of motion of the boat.

Draw a scale diagram to show the forces acting on the boat.

Write down the scale that you used.

The scale used is: _____ cm = _____ N

P8.2 Forces between objects

A Fill in the gaps to complete the sentences.

Forces can change the _____ of an object, change the _____ of an object, or start a

_____ object moving. Forces are measured in _____ .

A _____ force is a force that acts on objects only when they touch each other.

When two objects interact they always exert _____ and _____ forces on each other.

B Write down **one** example of each of the following effects of a force.

a A force can change the shape of an object. Example:

_____

_____

b A force can change the motion of an object. Example:

_____

_____

c A force can start an object moving that was at rest. Example:

_____

_____

C Compare **contact forces** with **non-contact forces**. Give **one** example of each type of force.

_____

_____

_____

D a Write down **Newton's third law**.

_____

_____

b Explain why the **two** forces acting on you as you sit on a chair writing an answer to this question are **not** an example of Newton's third law.

_____

_____

_____

c Describe how Newton's third law explains how you walk across the floor.

_____

_____

d Describe how Newton's third law explains how a space rocket takes off when fuel in the rocket is ignited.

_____

_____

_____

P8.3 Resultant forces

A Fill in the gaps to complete the sentences.

The resultant force is a single force that has the _____ effect as all the forces acting on an object.

An object stays at rest or moves with a steady speed when the resultant force on it is _____ .

The speed or direction of an object changes when the resultant force on it is _____ than

_____ .

If there are two forces acting on an object along the same line you _____ them if they act in the same

direction, and find the _____ if they act in opposite directions.

A _____ force diagram of an object shows the forces acting on it.

B Explain how the resultant force on a moving cyclist could be zero.

_____

_____

C a Here are some descriptions of the motion of objects. Circle the descriptions where the resultant force is zero.

stationary　　　　**speeding up**　　　　**slowing down**　　　　**moving at a steady speed**

b The table shows some pairs of forces that act along the same line.

Complete the table by finding the resultant force of each pair of forces.

Write the magnitude and the direction (left or right).

Force to the left in N	Force to the right in N	Resultant force magnitude in N	Resultant force direction (left or right?)
7	3		
10	20		
80	150		

D a You are floating on the surface of a swimming pool. Draw arrows as seen from the side to show the forces acting on you, and the free-body diagram of you.

The force of the water on you	The force of the Earth on you	A free-body diagram of you
●	●	●

b Explain how you know that the forces on you are balanced. How did you show this in the free-body diagram?

_____

_____

_____

P8.4 Moments at work

A Fill in the gaps to complete the sentences.

When a _____ acts on an object it can have a _____ effect, which is called a

_____ . The size of the turning effect depends on the size of the _____ and the

_____ between where the force acts and the _____ .

The size of a moment can be calculated using this equation:

moment (____) = _____

[You need to remember this equation.]

B The diagram shows a crowbar being used to lift a heavy object. The effort being used to lift the safe is 200 N and
the horizontal distance from the effort to the pivot is 0.50 m.

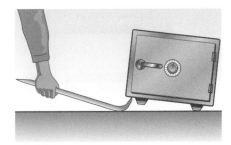

Draw and label the effort, the pivot, and the load on the diagram.

Calculate the moment being produced by the effort force.

moment = _____
The crowbar is in contact with the safe 0.10 m horizontally from the pivot.

Calculate the force acting on the safe due to the turning effect.

force = _____

Complete the table to show the force, distance, and moment for different tools.

Tool	Force in N	Perpendicular distance to pivot in m	Moment in N m
scissors	30	0.05	**a**
door handle	50	**b**	29
garden shears	**c**	0.30	12

Explain why it is easier to hold a heavy object close to your body rather than at arm's length. Sketch a diagram to
support your explanation.

_____

_____

P8.5 More about levers and gears

A Fill in the gaps to complete the sentences.

A lever acts as a force _____ if the effort force is a greater distance from the _____ than the load force.

Gears can be used to change the _____ _____ of a force. In a car, a _____ gear setting will give low speed and a _____ turning effect, while a _____ gear setting will give a higher speed and a _____ turning effect.

B The diagrams show simplified models of gears that connect a car engine to the wheels.

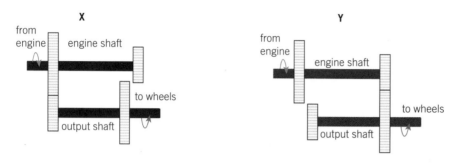

a Which diagram shows a high gear setting? _____

b Which gear setting, **X** or **Y**, provides the greatest turning effect on the car wheels? _____

C A student measured the force required (effort) to lift a series of weights (load) that were connected by a wheel and axle system, as shown. The results are shown in the table.

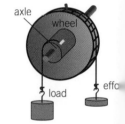

Load in N	50.0	40.0	30.0	20.0
Effort in N	16.6	14.0	10.2	7.04
Load to effort ratio				

a Calculate the load to effort ratio for each of the tests and complete the table.

b Calculate the mean value for the load to effort ratio for the wheel and axle system.

mean load to effort ratio = _____

c The experiment is repeated using a wheel with a greater radius.

Predict whether the load to effort ratio will be larger, smaller, or the same, and give a reason.

_____

_____

_____

P8.6 Centre of mass

A Fill in the gaps to complete the sentences.

The centre of mass of an object is the _____ where all the mass is concentrated.

For a uniform object such as a sphere or a cube, the centre of mass is in the _____ of the object.

A suspended object will stop swinging when the centre of mass is _____ the point of suspension.

The centre of mass of a symmetrical object is along its _____ of symmetry.

B Explain in terms of centre of mass why the height of a racing car is much smaller than the height of a family car.

_____

_____

C Put a dot in each object below where you expect its centre of mass to be.

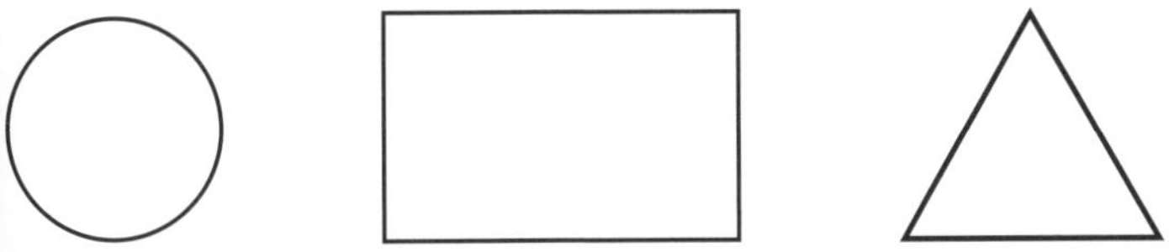

D High winds can be a problem for lorries. In the diagrams below, the centre of mass of the lorry and the pivot point are labelled.

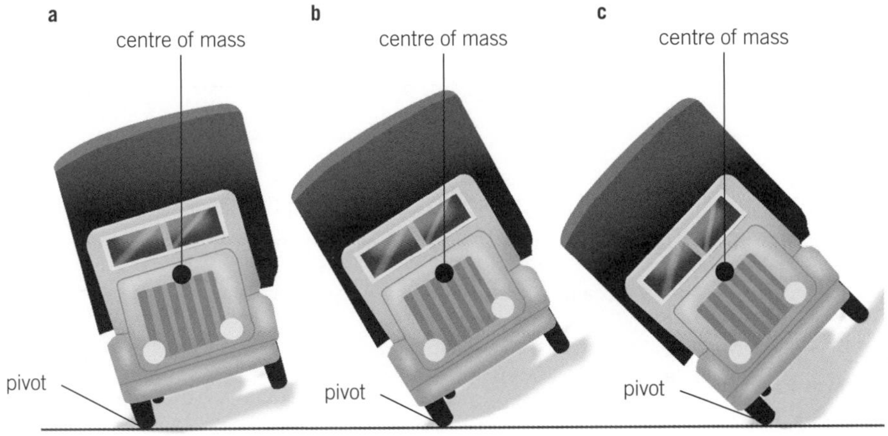

a centre of mass

b centre of mass

c centre of mass

pivot

pivot

pivot

Add an arrow to each diagram to show the force of the Earth (weight) on the lorry.

Use the diagrams to explain why a very strong wind is needed to topple a lorry.

_____

_____

_____

_____

P8.7 Moments and equilibrium

A Fill in the gaps to complete the sentences.

When a system is at rest and balanced, we say it is in _____.

The _____ of _____ states that for a system in equilibrium the sum of all of the

_____ _____ around any point is equal to the sum of the _____

_____ around that point.

B Two masses are placed on a uniform ruler of weight 2.0 N so that they are balanced, as shown in the diagram.

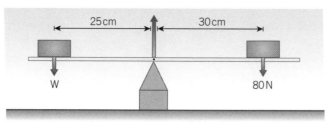

a Calculate the weight W of the object on the left.

weight $W =$ _____

b What is the size of force F?

HINT Remember the ruler is in equilibrium.

_____

c Explain why force F has no turning effect on the ruler.

_____

_____

C A student carries out an experiment to measure the mass of an unknown beam using the principle of moments. They place the beam on a pivot and balance it with a series of weights as shown in the diagram.

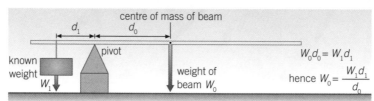

a Complete the table to show the weight of the beam for each measurement.

Known weight (W_1) in N	Distance from known weight to pivot (d_1) in cm	Balance distance (d_0) in cm	Weight of beam (W_0) in N
2.50	33.2	10	
3.00	22.6	8.5	
4.50	12.8	7.5	
5.00	10.0	6.0	

b Calculate the mean value for the weight of the beam.

weight = _____

P8.8 The parallelogram of forces

A Fill in the gaps to complete the sentences.

The parallelogram of forces is the _____ diagram of two force vectors.

The parallelogram of forces is used to find the _____ of two forces that do not act along the same line.

To make a parallelogram of forces diagram, you need a ruler, a pencil, a blank sheet of paper, and a _____ .

The resultant is the diagonal of the parallelogram that starts at the _____ of the two forces.

B Describe the type of situation where you need to use a parallelogram of forces, and the type of situation where you do not.

_____

_____

C A force of 60 N and a force of 40 N act on the same object. The angle between the forces is 30°.

a Draw a scale diagram to represent the forces on the object.

b Use the diagram to find the resultant force.

resultant force = _____ N

D Two tug boats pull a tanker along a river.

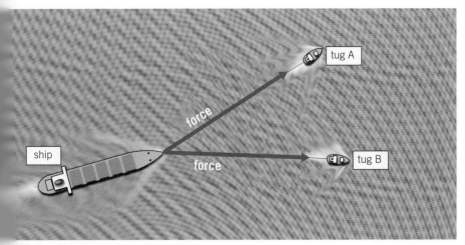

Draw the resultant force on the tanker.

In each of the situations below, describe the effect on the resultant force.

i Tug B pulls twice as hard as tug A.

_____

_____

ii The rope attached to tug A breaks.

_____

_____

P8.9 Resolution of forces

A Fill in the gaps to complete the sentences.

When you are resolving a force, you are finding two components that are at _____ to each other that have a resultant force that is equal to that force.

You can resolve a force in two perpendicular directions by drawing a _____ with adjacent sides along

the two directions so that the _____ represents the force vector.

The resultant force is zero for an object in _____.

An object at _____ is in equilibrium because the resultant force on it is zero.

B a You are sitting on a hillside. Write down the angle between the slope and the normal component of your weight. _____

b Compare the magnitude of the normal force when you are sitting on flat ground with the normal force when you are sitting on the hillside.

_____

_____

C The arrow shows a resultant force of 10 N. Use a scale diagram to calculate the horizontal and vertical components of the force that is equal to this resultant force.

D A student puts a box on a ramp. He then lifts the end of the ramp until the box is just about to move.

a Draw and label the forces that are acting on the box along the slope and normal to the slope. Two of these forces are components.

b Give the two measurements that the student needs to make to measure the frictional force on the box, and explain why.

_____

_____

c The student replaces the box with a trolley. Explain the effect on the height the student needs to lift the ramp to make the trolley move.

_____

_____

P8 Practice questions

01 Explain why the moment of a force is a vector but temperature is **not** a vector. [2 marks]

_____

_____

02 Circle the contact forces in the list below. [2 marks]

gravity   **friction**   **tension**

magnetic attraction   **air resistance**

03 **Figure 1** shows some forces acting on a box.

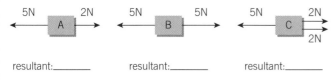

resultant:_____   resultant:_____   resultant:_____

Figure 1

03.1 Draw an arrow (where appropriate) to show the resultant force acting on each box. Label with the magnitude of the force. [3 marks]

03.2 Explain which of the boxes is in equilibrium. [2 marks]

_____

_____

03.3 **Table 1** describes what each box **A**, **B**, and **C** in **03.1** is doing before the forces are applied to them.

Table 1

Box	What the box is doing	What the box will start to do
A	not moving	
B	moving at 3 m/s to the left	
C	moving at 3 m/s to the left	

Complete the table to describe what each box will start to do when the forces shown in **03.1** are applied to them. [3 marks]

04 A wheelbarrow is used to move soil from one part of a garden to another as shown in **Figure 2**. The wheelbarrow is being held in equilibrium.

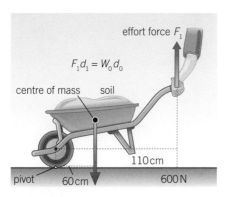

Figure 2

04.1 Write down **two** conditions that must be met for the wheelbarrow to be in equilibrium. [2 marks]

_____

_____

_____

04.2 Calculate the size of the effort force F_1 acting on the handles. [2 marks]

_____

_____

04.3 To empty out the barrow, the handles are lifted higher and the barrow tilts forwards.

Describe and explain what happens to the size of the moment about the pivot caused by the weight of the soil, as the wheelbarrow tilts forwards. [2 marks]

_____

_____

_____

05 You are lying on a sofa and then get up and stand on the floor.

Compare the magnitudes of the reaction forces acting on you when you are lying on the sofa and when you are standing on the floor. [1 mark]

_____

06 A child sits on a swing made from an old tyre (**Figure 3**).

06.1 Write down what you know about the position of the centre of mass of the child and swing. [1 mark]

_____

_____

Figure 3

06.2 A friend of the child pushes the tyre to the left so that the angle between the rope and the vertical is 30°. The weight of the child and tyre is 50 N.

Use a free-body scale diagram to find the tension in the rope. [4 marks]

P8 Checklist

	Student Book	☺	☺	☹
I can write down what displacement is.	8.1			
I can write down what a vector quantity is.	8.1			
I can write down what a scalar quantity is.	8.1			
I can describe how to represent a vector quantity.	8.1			
I can write down what forces can do.	8.2			
I can write down the unit of force.	8.2			
I can write down what a contact force is.	8.2			
I can describe the forces being exerted when two objects interact.	8.2			
I can describe what a resultant force is.	8.3			
I can describe what happens if the resultant force on an object is zero.	8.3			
I can describe what happens if the resultant force on an object is greater than zero.	8.3			
I can calculate the resultant force when an object is acted on by two forces acting along the same line.	8.3			
I can describe the action of a lever.	8.4			
I can calculate the moment caused by a force.	8.4			
I can describe how a lever can be used to multiply a force.	8.5			
I can explain how gears can be used to increase or decrease turning effects.	8.5			
I can write down what the centre of mass of an object is.	8.6			
I can write down where the centre of mass of a metre ruler is.	8.6			
I can find the centre of mass of an object suspended from a fixed point.	8.6			
I can find the centre of mass of a symmetrical object.	8.6			
I can use the principle of moments to analyse systems in equilibrium.	8.7			
I can write down what a parallelogram of forces is.	8.8			
I can write down what a parallelogram of forces is used for.	8.8			
I can write down what is needed to draw a scale diagram of a parallelogram of forces.	8.8			
I can use a parallelogram of forces to find the resultant of two forces.	8.8			
I can describe what resolving a force means.	8.9			
I can describe how to resolve a force into two components.	8.9			
I can define equilibrium.	8.9			
I can explain why an object at rest is in equilibrium.	8.9			

P9.1 Speed and distance–time graphs

A Fill in the gaps to complete the sentences.

You can calculate speed using this equation:

$$\text{speed} (\underline{\hspace{1cm}}) = \frac{\overline{\hspace{6cm}}}{\underline{\hspace{6cm}}}$$

[You need to remember this equation.]

The distance–time graph for a _____ object is a horizontal straight line, and the distance–time graph for

an object moving with a _____ _____ is a straight line that slopes upwards.

The _____ of a distance-time graph for an object tells you the object's speed.

B An ice skater glides across the ice and travels a distance of 11 m in 2.7 s.

a Calculate his speed.

speed = _____ m/s

b Give an assumption that you need to make in order to calculate this speed.

_____

C A skateboarder travels at 5.5 m/s.

a Calculate how far he travels in 15 s.

distance travelled = _____ m

b Calculate the time it takes him to travel 70 m.

time = _____ s

D Use the data on the graph to describe the motion of the object in section **A** of the graph and compare it with the motion in section **B**.

_____

_____

_____

_____

_____

_____

P9.2 Velocity and acceleration

A Fill in the gaps to complete the sentences.

Velocity is the speed in a given _____ .

A _____ quantity is a physical quantity that has magnitude and direction. A _____ quantity is a physical quantity that has magnitude only.

You can calculate acceleration using this equation:

$$\text{acceleration (\_\_\_\_)} = \frac{\rule{6cm}{0.4pt}}{\rule{5cm}{0.4pt}}$$

[You need to remember this equation.]

Deceleration is the change of velocity per second when an object _____ _____ .

An object moving in a circle with a constant speed has a _____ that is constantly changing.

B a Explain the difference between speed and velocity.

_____

  b Circle the vectors in the list below.

| **10 m/s north** | **25 mph** | **38 mph south** | **10 m/s** | **38 mph** |

C a A car travels in a circle of radius 25 m in 20 seconds.

  Calculate its speed.

  $\pi = 3.14$

  speed = _____ m/s

  b Explain why the car is accelerating.

  _____

  _____

  c Compare the speed and velocity of the car when it is at opposite sides of the circle.

  _____

  _____

D a A plane takes off. Its velocity changes from rest to a speed of 100 m/s over half a minute.

  Calculate the acceleration of the plane. Give the unit.

  acceleration _____

  b The plane prepares to land. Its velocity changes from 155 m/s to 140 m/s over 2 minutes.

  Calculate the acceleration of the plane. Give the unit.

  acceleration = _____

P9.3 More about velocity–time graphs

A Fill in the gaps to complete the sentences.

You can use a _____ _____ linked to a computer to measure velocity changes.

The _____ of the line on a velocity-time graph tells you the acceleration. If the line is horizontal the

acceleration is _____ .

If the object has a positive acceleration the line has a _____ _____ .

If the object is decelerating the line has a _____ _____ .

The area under the line on a velocity–time graph tells you the _____ _____ .

B Describe **one** advantage and **one** disadvantage of using a motion sensor to produce a velocity–time graph.

_____

_____

C Complete the table to explain how to interpret a velocity–time graph.

If the line on the graph is…	…then the object is…
…straight, and going up	
…straight, and going down	
…straight, and horizontal	

D Here is the velocity–time graph for a train travelling between two stations.

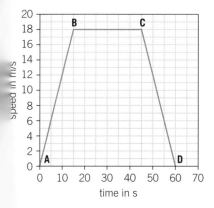

Calculate the acceleration between points **A** and **B**.

Calculate the total distance travelled.

Explain how you can write down the acceleration between points **C** and **D** without doing a calculation.

_____

_____

_____

P9.4 Analysing motion graphs

A Fill in the gaps to complete the sentences.

You can find the speed from a distance–time graph by finding the _____ of the line on the graph.

You can find the acceleration from a velocity–time graph by finding the _____ of the line on the graph.

You can find the distance travelled from a velocity–time graph by finding the _____ _____ the line on the graph.

If the speed is changing, you can find the speed at any instant in time from a distance–time graph by finding the

_____ of the _____ to the line on the graph.

B Compare a horizontal line on a distance–time graph and a horizontal line on a speed–time graph.

_____

_____

_____

C An object travels a distance of 20 m in 10 s at a steady speed, and is then stationary for 10 s. Then its speed steadily increases for 10 s.

Describe the gradient of a velocity–time graph for the motion by completing the table below.

During...	The gradient of the line on the graph will be...
0–10 seconds	
10–20 seconds	
20–30 seconds	

D A student produces distance–time graphs for two objects, **X** and **Y**.

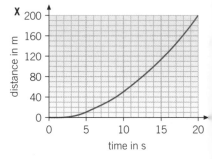

a Calculate the speed of object **X** at 10 s.

b Calculate the speed of object **Y** at 10 s.

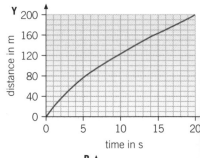

c Here are the two velocity–time graphs for objects **X** and **Y**. Suggest and explain which graph describes the motion of object **X**.

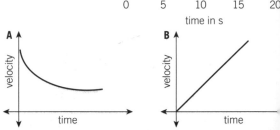

_____

_____

P9 Practice questions

01 Complete **Table 1** by calculating speed, distance, or time. [3 marks]

Table 1

Steady speed in m/s	Distance in m	Time in s
	52	7.0
12		0.02
115	3000	

02 Riya drops her phone. It accelerates from a vertical speed of 0 m/s to a speed of 0.5 m/s in a time of 0.05 s. Calculate the acceleration. [3 marks]

_____
_____
_____

03 **Figure 1** is a graph showing a person's journey.

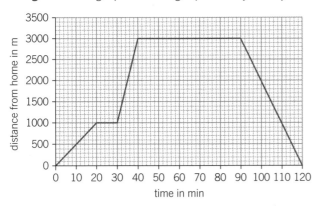

Figure 1

3.1 Write down **one** of the distances from home at which the person was stationary. [1 mark]

_____

3.2 Calculate the fastest speed shown on the graph. [2 marks]

_____
_____

3.3 Suggest how the measurements were obtained for this graph. [2 marks]

_____
_____

4 **Figure 2** shows the velocity–time graph for a cyclist.

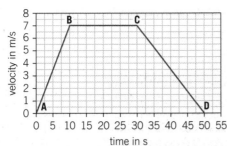

Figure 2

04.1 Use the graph to write down or calculate the acceleration of the cyclist between points **A**, **B**, **C**, and **D**. [5 marks]

_____
_____
_____
_____
_____
_____
_____

04.2 A student uses a velocity of 7 m/s, a time of 50 s, and the equation distance = speed × time to calculate that the distance travelled by the cyclist is 350 m.

Explain why this method is **incorrect**. [1 mark]

_____
_____

04.3 Calculate the **correct** distance travelled by the cyclist. [2 marks]

_____
_____

04.4 The cyclist travels in a large circle at a steady speed of 5 m/s. Suggest and explain one other measurement that you need to make to calculate the acceleration of the cyclist. [3 marks]

_____
_____
_____

05 **Figure 3** shows a distance–time graph for a drag racer.

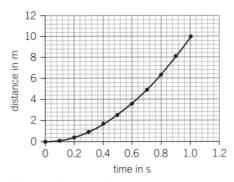

Figure 3

Use the graph to calculate the speed of the racer after 0.5 s. [3 marks]

_____
_____
_____
_____

P9 Checklist

	Student Book	☺	☻	☹
I can calculate speed is calculated for an object moving at constant speed.	9.1			
I can use a distance–time graph to determine whether an object is stationary or moving at constant speed.	9.1			
I can write down what the gradient of the line on a distance–time graph can tell you.	9.1			
I can use the equation for constant speed to calculate distance moved or time taken.	9.1			
I can write down the difference between speed and velocity.	9.2			
I can calculate the acceleration of an object.	9.2			
I can write down the difference between acceleration and deceleration.	9.2			
I can explain that motion in a circle involves constant speed but changing velocity.	9.2			
I can measure velocity change.	9.3			
I can write down what a horizontal line on a velocity–time graph tells you.	9.3			
I can use a velocity–time graph to work out whether an object is accelerating or decelerating.	9.3			
I can write down what the area under a velocity–time graph tells you.	9.3			
I can calculate speed from a distance–time graph where the speed is constant.	9.4			
I can calculate speed from a distance–time graph where the speed is changing.	9.4			
I can calculate acceleration from a velocity–time graph.	9.4			
I can calculate distance from a velocity–time graph.	9.4			

P10.1 Force and acceleration

A Fill in the gaps to complete the sentences.

If the resultant force on an object increases, the acceleration will _____ , as long as the _____ stays the same.

If two objects of different masses have the same resultant force acting on them, the acceleration of the object with the bigger mass will be _____ .

You can calculate the resultant force acting on an object using this equation:

resultant force (_____) = _____

[You need to remember this equation.]

The inertia of an object is its tendency to stay at _____ or in _____ motion.

B Describe how the acceleration of an object depends on the force and the mass.

_____

_____

_____

_____

C Write a sentence to describe **inertial mass**.

_____

_____

D a Calculate the resultant force on a ball that has a mass of 105 g and is accelerating at 3.20 m/s². Include the units.

resultant force = _____

b You exert the same resultant force on another ball that has a mass of 210 g.

Calculate the acceleration of this ball.

acceleration = _____ m/s²

c Explain whether the ball in part **a** or the ball in part **b** has the greater inertia.

_____

_____

d Explain what you would need to do to the resultant force to accelerate the 210 g ball at 3.20 m/s².

_____

_____

P10.2 Weight and terminal velocity

A Fill in the gaps to complete the sentences.

The weight of an object is the _____ acting on the object due to gravity. The mass is the quantity of

_____ in the object.

If there is only gravity acting on an object, then it will accelerate at about _____ m/s^2.

When an object falls, it eventually reaches _____ velocity. This happens when the weight equals the

_____ force on the object. At this velocity, the resultant force on the object is _____ .

B a A person reads their 'weight' on some bathroom scales. The measurement is 75 kg. Explain in terms of physics why this is wrong.

_____

_____

b Complete the table with the correct values of mass and weight.

Mass in kg	Gravitational field strength in N/kg	Weight in N
0.2	10	
	27	30
0.035	1.6	

C a The only force acting on an object is gravity.

Write down the acceleration of the object.

acceleration = _____ m/s^2

b Explain why a stone dropped into a deep lake will not have the same acceleration.

_____

_____

c The stone is dropped from a point 1 m above the surface of the lake.

Describe and explain what happens to the velocity of the stone from the point it is dropped until it hits the bottom of the lake.

_____

_____

_____

_____

d Sketch a graph to show how the speed of the stone changes with time. Mark an 'x' on the part of the graph where the resultant force is zero.

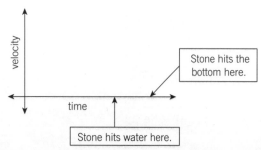

P10.3 Forces and braking

A Fill in the gaps to complete the sentences.

Friction and air resistance oppose the _____ force of a vehicle.

The stopping distance of a vehicle depends on the _____ distance and the _____ distance.

Poor weather conditions, poor vehicle maintenance, and speed affect the _____ distance. Poor reaction

time and high speed both affect the _____ distance.

You can work out the braking force of a vehicle using this equation:

force (_____) = _____

B a Complete the table by defining each distance and stating **three** factors that affect each one. One has been
done for you.

Distance	Definition	Depends on
braking distance		1. speed 2. 3.
thinking distance		1. speed 2. 3.

b Describe a situation in which a lorry might have the same stopping distance as a car.

_____

_____

a Calculate the force of the brakes on a car of mass 1000 kg that has a deceleration of 4 m/s². Include the unit.

force = _____

b The car is initially travelling at 30 m/s. It needs to stop in a distance of 120 m to avoid an accident. Explain
whether the car will avoid the accident.

_____

_____

c Suggest why the braking distance of a car is not proportional to the speed.

_____

_____

P10.4 Momentum

A Fill in the gaps to complete the sentences.

You can calculate momentum using this equation:

momentum (_____) = _____

[You need to remember this equation.]

A closed system is a system in which the total momentum before an event is _____ _____ _____ the total momentum after the event. This is called _____ of momentum.

B A lorry has twice the mass of a car.

Explain how both the lorry and the car can have the same momentum.

_____

_____

_____

C A plane of mass 300 000 kg is taxiing on a runway at 2 m/s.

Calculate the momentum of the plane. Include the unit.

momentum = _____

D A student investigates two colliding trolleys. Motion sensors measure the speed of the trolleys. Before the collision, trolley **X** (mass 300 g) moves with a velocity of 2 m/s to the left, and collides with trolley **Y** (mass 150 g) moving to the right. After the collision, both trolleys stop.

a Calculate the velocity of trolley **Y** before the collision.

velocity of trolley **Y** before the collision = _____ m/s

b Write an assumption that you made when doing this calculation.

_____

c In a different collision, the two trolleys stick together after the collision and move together to the left. Compare the motion of the trolleys before the collision in this experiment with their motion in part **a**.

_____

_____

P10.5 Using conservation of momentum

A Fill in the gaps to complete the sentences.

The law of _____ of momentum states that, when no external _____ act on a system of

objects, the _____ _____ is always conserved.

When an object breaks apart due to internal forces, we describe this as an _____. Parts of the object will

move off at different speeds in _____ _____. If the object was stationary before this event,

then the total momentum after the event will be _____.

B A man, standing on a small boat as shown, tries to leap across the gap between his boat and one nearby.
Explain why the gap between the boats increases and the man falls into the water.

_____
_____
_____
_____

C Two ice hockey players are moving in the same direction when they collide. The first player has a mass of 80 kg and is moving at 2.0 m/s; the second player has a mass of 75 kg and is moving at 6.0 m/s when he hits the first player.

Assuming the players 'tangle together', calculate their speed immediately after the impact.

HINT In this question the 'objects' are moving in the same direction so their momentums add during the collision.

_____
_____
_____

D To manoeuvre in space, an astronaut fires jets of gas from nozzles pointing in different directions.

Explain how this allows the astronaut to move in a chosen direction.

_____
_____
_____
_____

P10.6 Impact forces

A Fill in the gaps to complete the sentences.

The size of the _____ on an object during an impact depends on the _____ of the impact.

For any collision, the shorter the impact time, the _____ the force experienced.

The force experienced during a collision is related to the change in _____ by the equation:

$$\text{force} = \frac{\text{change in} \underline{\hspace{2cm}}}{\text{time of collision}} \quad \text{or} \quad F = \frac{\overline{\hspace{1cm}}}{\Delta t}$$

During a collision between two objects the forces produced between the objects are _____ in size but

_____ in direction, and the forces have the same duration. This explains why the change of momentum

of one object is matched by an equal and _____ change in momentum of the other.

B The diagram shows two cars colliding head-on at high speed in a crash simulator.

20 m/s →   0 m/s

X   Y

Before the collision, car **X**, which has a mass of 550 kg, was travelling at a velocity of 20 m/s to the right. Immediately after the impact, the cars merge together and move at a velocity of 5.0 m/s to the right. The impact lasts 0.25 s.

a Calculate the deceleration of car **X** during the impact.

deceleration = _____ m/s²

b Calculate the average size of the force acting on car **X** during the impact.

average force = _____ N

c What is the average size of the force acting on car **Y** during the impact?

_____

C The two cars **X** and **Y** from activity **B** now have crumple zones fitted to their fronts. These do not significantly increase the cars' masses. The cars then undergo the same test as in activity **B**.

a Explain how the crumple zones reduce the size of the forces during the collision.

_____

_____

_____

b Without any further calculation, write the velocity of the cars immediately after the impact.

_____

c Explain your answer to part **b**.

_____

_____

P10.7 Safety first

A Fill in the gaps to complete the sentences.

Many safety measures used to reduce harm in vehicle impacts are designed to _____ the

_____ of the impact.

Seat belts are designed to stop the driver or passengers hitting the _____ or the seat in front. Such

an impact would happen over a very short _____ and so produce a very large _____.

The seat belt is wide and goes over a large part of the body, so that it has a _____ area, reducing the

_____ experienced by the passenger.

Modern steering wheels and dashboards are fitted with _____ _____, which inflate during

a collision. These increase the impact time and so _____ the force on the chest and head of the driver

and front passenger.

B Label the diagram to show the safety features used in modern cars.

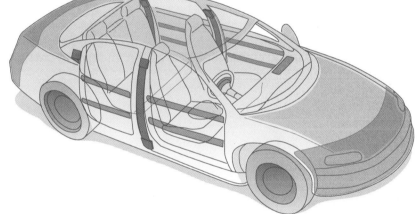

C The graph shows the relationship between thinking distance, braking
distance, stopping distance, and speed for a typical car.

Explain, in terms of forces and the equations of motion, why:

• the thinking distance is proportional to the car's speed.

_____

_____

_____

• the braking distance is proportional to the square of the speed.

_____

_____

_____

_____

_____

P10.8 Forces and elasticity

A Fill in the gaps to complete the sentences.

An object is _____ if it returns to its original shape after you remove the force that you have used to deform it.

The extension of an object is the _____ between the length when you stretch it and its original length.

The extension of a spring is _____ _____ to the force applied to it. This is only true if you do

not go beyond the limit of _____ . This is a _____ relationship.

If you *do* go beyond the limit of _____ , then the relationship becomes _____–_____ , and

the force and extension are no longer _____ .

B a Describe and explain what you could do to show that the material used to make plastic bags shows plastic, and not elastic, behaviour.

_____

_____

b Name the **two** quantities that are no longer proportional if the limit of proportionality is exceeded.

_____

C a A student stretches a spring with a spring constant of 40 N/m. The spring is 3.0 cm long at the start, and 4.5 cm long after the student applies a force.

Calculate the force applied.

force = _____ N

b Calculate the length of the spring if the force on the spring is trebled.

length = _____ cm

D This graph shows the extension of a sample as a student increases the force applied to the sample.

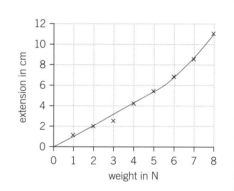

a Explain how you know that the sample obeys Hooke's law.

_____

b Describe what the student would observe if she hung weights of up to 6 N on the sample and then removed the weights.

_____

_____

c Calculate the spring constant of the sample.

spring constant = _____ N/m

P10 Practice questions

01 Explain how and why speed affects the stopping distance of a car. [6 marks]

_____

_____

_____

_____

_____

_____

02.1 Complete **Table 1** by calculating the resultant force, mass, or acceleration. [3 marks]

Table 1

Mass	Acceleration in m/s^2	Force
1.3 g	2	
1.5 kg		1 kN
	7×10^{-3}	2 N

02.2 Explain how you know that the mass in **Table 1** is the inertial mass. [1 mark]

_____

_____

03 A student drops a light ball. One of the forces acting on the ball is the force of the Earth on it.

Table 2 shows the speed of the ball as it falls.

Table 2

Time in s	Speed in m/s
0.0	0
0.1	1
0.2	2
0.3	3
0.4	3
0.5	3

03.1 Write down the value of the terminal velocity.

_____ [1 mark]

03.2 Describe and explain the motion of the ball between 0.3 s and 0.5 s. [3 marks]

_____

_____

_____

04 An aircraft of mass 250 000 kg lands on an aircraft carrier. There is a hook at the bottom of the aircraft that latches onto thick wires, which stretch to bring the aircraft to a stop. The aircraft lands at a speed of 60 m/s and comes to a stop over a distance of 50 m.

04.1 Calculate the deceleration of the aircraft. [3 marks]

_____

_____

04.2 Calculate the force of the wire on the aircraft. [3 marks]

_____

_____

04.3 The wire extends by 10 m.

Calculate the spring constant of the wire. [2 marks]

_____

_____

04.4 Calculate the momentum of the aircraft as it latches onto the wire. [2 marks]

_____

_____

05 A group of students designed an experiment to test the effectiveness of an air bag on reducing the force of impact. They dropped an egg onto a hard surface and then another egg onto a partially inflated balloon.

In the first test, an egg of mass 50.0 g was dropped from a height of 1.00 m above the ground onto a hard surface and it broke upon impact.

05.1 Calculate the velocity of the egg when it hit the floor. ($g = 9.8$ m/s^2) [3 marks]

_____

_____

_____

05.2 Calculate the momentum of the egg just as it hit the floor. [2 marks]

_____

_____

05.3 The second egg, also of mass 50.0 g, was dropped from a height of 1.00 m above the top surface of a partially inflated balloon. Using a slow-motion camera, the students found that the egg was brought to a stop in a time of 0.40 s.

Calculate the average force causing the egg to decelerate during this impact. [3 marks]

_____

_____

_____

_____

05.4 Explain why the egg broke during the first test but not during the second. [2 marks]

_____

_____

P10 Checklist

	Student Book	☺	☺	☹
I can describe how the acceleration of an object depends on the size of the resultant force acting upon it.	10.1			
I can describe the effect that the mass of an object has on its acceleration.	10.1			
I can describe how to calculate the resultant force on an object from its acceleration and its mass.	10.1			
I can write down what the inertia of an object means.	10.1			
I can describe the difference between mass and weight.	10.2			
I can describe and explain the motion of a falling object acted on only by gravity.	10.2			
I can write down what terminal velocity means.	10.2			
I can write down what can be said about the resultant force acting on an object that is falling at terminal velocity.	10.2			
I can describe the forces that oppose the driving force of a vehicle.	10.3			
I can write down what the stopping distance of a vehicle depends on.	10.3			
I can write down what can increase the stopping distance of a vehicle.	10.3			
I can describe how to estimate the braking force of a vehicle.	10.3			
I can calculate momentum.	10.4			
I can write down the unit of momentum.	10.4			
I can describe what momentum means in a closed system.	10.4			
I can describe what happens when two objects push each other apart.	10.4			
I can use the principle of conservation of momentum to analyse 'explosions'.	10.4			
I can use the principle of conservation of momentum to analyse collisions.	10.5			
I can use changes in momentum to find the size of impact forces.	10.6			
I can explain how safety features in cars reduce the force experienced by a passenger during a collision.	10.7			
I can explain how cushioning materials reduce the force during an impact.	10.7			
I can write down what 'elastic' means.	10.8			
I can describe how to measure the extension of an object when it is stretched.	10.8			
I can describe how the extension of a spring changes with the force applied to it.	10.8			
I can write down what the limit of proportionality of a spring means.	10.8			
I can write down what 'elastic' means.	10.8			
I can describe how to measure the extension of an object when it is stretched.	10.8			
I can describe how the extension of a spring changes with the force applied to it.	10.8			
I can write down what the limit of proportionality of a spring means.	10.8			
I can write down what 'elastic' means.	10.8			
I can describe how to measure the extension of an object when it is stretched.	10.8			
I can describe how the extension of a spring changes with the force applied to it.	10.8			
I can write down what the limit of proportionality of a spring means.	10.8			
I can write down what 'elastic' means.	10.8			
I can describe how to measure the extension of an object when it is stretched.	10.8			
I can describe how the extension of a spring changes with the force applied to it.	10.8			
I can write down what the limit of proportionality of a spring means.	10.8			

P11.1 Pressure and surfaces

A Fill in the gaps to complete the sentences.

Pressure is caused when a _____ acts over an _____ . High pressure can damage or cut into materials.

To find the pressure acting on a surface we can use this equation:

pressure (_____)= $\dfrac{\rule{3cm}{0.4pt}}{\rule{3cm}{0.4pt}}$ or $p = \dfrac{\rule{1cm}{0.4pt}}{\rule{1cm}{0.4pt}}$ *[You need to remember this equation.]*

B Describe how you could find out the pressure that different animals cause on the floor when they stand still. How could you extend this investigation to find the pressure they cause as they walk?

_____

_____

_____

C During a training session, an ice skater travels across an ice rink wearing skates with a blade of length 30.0 cm and width 3.00 mm. As he skates the blades cut small grooves into the ice.

a Calculate the pressure (in pascals) caused on the ice when a skater of mass 80.0 kg stands on both feet. Gravitational field strength $g = 9.8$ N/kg

_____

_____

_____

b After the training session a 'Zamboni' ice re-surfacer is used to polish the ice and remove any rough surface. This is a vehicle similar to a small tractor but with a blade to 'shave' the ice and a water sprayer to then form a new layer of smooth ice. The Zamboni has a mass of 2000 kg.

Explain why the Zamboni does not cut into the ice like the skater in part **a** did.

water sprayer

blade

brush

ice surface

_____

_____

_____

D A bicycle and rider with a total mass of 55 kg has two tyres in contact with the ground. The contact area for each tyre is 15 cm².

Gravitational field strength $g = 9.8$ N/kg

Calculate the pressure in the tyres needed to support the bicycle and rider. (Assume the pressure is the same in both tyres.)

HINT The pressure in the tyres must be equal to the pressure that the bicycle and rider exert on the ground.

_____

_____

_____

Explain what will happen to the area of the tyres in contact with the ground if there is a small puncture and the pressure in one of the tyres starts to decrease slowly.

_____

_____

A Fill in the gaps to complete the sentences.

The pressure in a liquid increases with _____. This is because as you travel deeper into the liquid the

_____ of all of the liquid above you increases.

To find the pressure at a certain depth in a liquid we use the relationship:

pressure due to column of liquid (N/m²)

= height of column (m) × _____ × _____ or p = _____ × ρ × g

B The diagram shows jets of water (density 1000 kg/m³) squirting out of a bottle through small holes.

Gravitational field strength = 9.8 N/kg

a Explain why all of the jets of water squirt out to the same distance.

_____

_____

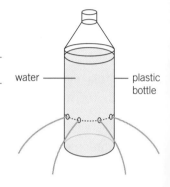

water —— —— plastic bottle

b The holes are all 15 cm below the initial level of the water.

Calculate the initial pressure acting on the water at the holes due to the water above it.

pressure = _____ Pa

C The diagram shows the design of a window for a submarine that is used to explore deep underwater. The pressure inside the submarine is kept at a constant 100 kPa while the outside pressure can reach as high as 1000 kPa.

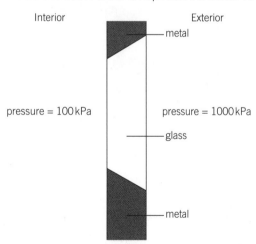

Interior   Exterior
                  —— metal

pressure = 100 kPa   pressure = 1000 kPa

                  —— glass

                  —— metal

a The area of the exterior surface of the window is 0.25 m².

Calculate the force acting on the outside of the window when the water pressure is 1000 kPa.

_____

b The area of the interior surface of the window is 0.20 m².

Calculate the force acting on the inside of the window.

_____

c Use your values from parts **a** and **b** to help explain why the window is shaped in the way it is.

_____

_____

P11.3 Atmospheric pressure

A Fill in the gaps to complete the sentences.

Atmospheric pressure is caused by air _____ colliding with _____. Although each collision

provides only a tiny _____, there are billions of these collisions each second.

Atmospheric pressure _____ with altitude. Once reason for this is that the density of the atmosphere

_____ with height, so there are _____ molecules.

The atmosphere extends to a height of approximately _____ from the Earth's surface.

B The graph shows atmospheric pressure against altitude above sea level.

a What would be the change in pressure as you climbed from sea level to the top of the highest mountain in France, Mont Blanc, which reaches 4800 metres above sea level?

_____

_____

_____

b Calculate the average density of the air between sea level and 4800 m.

> **HINT** Remember to use the change in pressure, rather than the pressure at 4800 m.

average density of the air = _____ kg/m^3

C Venus has a thick gaseous atmosphere containing large amounts of carbon dioxide. The table below shows the relationship between the atmospheric pressure of Venus and height above its surface.

Height above surface in km	0	5	10	15	20	25	30	35	40	45	50
Atmospheric pressure in kPa	9210	6665	4739	3304	2252	1493	985.1	591.7	350.1	197.9	106.6

a Plot a graph on a sheet of graph paper to show the relationship between atmospheric pressure and height above the surface for Venus.

> **HINT** Choose the scales carefully. You will need to round the pressure values in order to plot them.

Compare the graph to that for the Earth's atmosphere (the graph in activity **B**).

> **HINT** Mention the pattern and the values in your comparison.

_____

_____

_____

Calculate the average density of Venus's atmosphere between 0 and 5 km above the surface.

Gravitational field strength on Venus = 8.9 N/kg

average density = _____ kg/m^3

P11.4 Upthrust and flotation

A Fill in the gaps to complete the sentences.

When an object is placed in a _____ such as water, an upward force called _____ acts on it.

This force is caused by the difference in _____ between the top and the bottom of the object.

When an object floats, the upthrust acting on it is equal to the _____ of the object. If an object sinks

then its weight must be _____ than the upthrust.

B A student measures the upthrust acting on a range of rocks when placed in water, by weighing each rock and then lowering it into water so that it is completely below the surface and then re-weighing it. The results are shown in the table.

Object	Weight in air in N	Weight in water in N	Upthrust in N
rock A	6.3	4.3	
rock B	12.1	9.4	
rock C	14.3	11.1	

a Suggest the resolution of the newtonmeter that the student uses in the experiment. _____

b Complete the table to give the upthrust for the three rocks.

c The student now repeats the experiment but this time lowers the objects into oil, which has a lower density than water.

Suggest how the results of the experiment would be different using oil, giving your reasons.

_____

_____

_____

C The diagram shows a submarine below the ocean surface. The submarine is travelling at a constant depth beneath the surface. It has a mass of 150×10^3 kg.

Gravitational field strength = 9.8 N/kg

water surface

submarine

ocean floor

a What is the size of the upthrust acting on the submarine?

_____

b Add arrows to the diagram show the relative size of the pressure at the top and bottom surface of the submarine.

c Explain why this pressure difference causes the submarine to remain at the same depth in the ocean.

_____

_____

_____

_____

P11 Practice questions

01 A monster truck is used in a stunt show. The truck has four huge wheels and weighs 40 500 N. When driving across a flat surface the wheels make an area of contact with the ground of 0.05 m² each.

01.1 Calculate the pressure acting on the ground due to the monster truck. Include an appropriate unit.
[3 marks]

_____

_____

01.2 During a stunt, a shard of metal pierces the tyre. There is a hole of 2.0 mm² where the shard sticks into the tyre and is exposed to its internal pressure.

Calculate the force, in newtons, which acts on the metal shard due to the tyre pressure. [2 marks]

_____

_____

02 **Figure 1** shows a curved tube containing water and oil, which have different densities. The heights of the liquids are at different level levels.

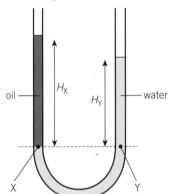

Figure 1

02.1 Compare the pressures at points X and Y, which are at the same level. [1 mark]

_____

_____

02.2 The height H_Y is measured to be 12.0 cm. Calculate the pressure at point Y due to the weight of the water above it.

Density of water = 1000 kg/m³, gravitational field strength = 9.8 N/kg [3 marks]

_____

_____

02.3 The height H_X is measured to be 14.2 cm. Determine the density of the oil. [3 marks]

_____

_____

_____

02.4 A small quantity of salt is added to the water. This causes the density of the water to increase.

Describe what you would observe happen to the levels of the liquids. [2 marks]

_____

_____

_____

03 A small submarine is used to take tourists to view a coral reef on the ocean floor. The submarine submerges so that its bottom surface is 12.0 m below sea level. The passengers have a clear view of the coral through a large glass panel on the base of the submarine. The submarine has a mass of 15 000 kg including its passengers.

Density of seawater = 1030 kg/m³, gravitational field strength = 9.8 N/kg

03.1 The pressure at the surface of the ocean is 100 kPa. Calculate the total pressure at a depth of 12.0 m below sea level. [3 marks]

_____

_____

03.2 The glass viewing panel has a surface area of 2.4 m² exposed to the sea.

Calculate the force acting on the panel due to the external pressure. [2 marks]

_____

_____

03.3 The internal pressure of the submarine is kept at 100 kPa to keep the passengers comfortable. Calculate the resultant force acting on the glass panel due to the pressure difference between the interior and exterior. [2 marks]

_____

_____

03.4 While the passengers are observing the coral, the submarine stays a constant distance from the seabed.

Give the size of the upthrust acting on the submarine while it is stationary. [1 mark]

_____

03.5 Explain the origin of this upthrust force in terms of pressure acting on the surfaces of the submarine. [4 marks]

_____

_____

_____

_____

_____

_____

P11 Checklist

	Student Book	☺	☺	☹
I can calculate the pressure acting on a surface.	11.1			
I can use the correct unit for pressure.	11.1			
I can explain how the pressure on a surface can be increased or decreased.	11.1			
I can describe why the pressure in a liquid increases with depth.	11.2			
I can calculate the pressure at a point in a liquid using the depth, the density of the liquid, and the gravitational field strength.	11.2			
I can describe how the Earth's atmosphere exerts a pressure on objects.	11.3			
I can describe how atmospheric pressure varies with altitude.	11.3			
I can calculate the average density of air using differences in pressure and height.	11.3			
I can explain why an upthrust force acts on a submerged or partially submerged object.	11.4			
I can describe how the density of a liquid will affect the upthrust it provides.	11.4			
I can explain why an object floats or sinks in a liquid.	11.4			
I can explain how objects made from material denser than water can be made to float.	11.4			

P12.1 The nature of waves

A Fill in the gaps to complete the sentences.

You can use waves to transfer _____ and energy.

A wave that oscillates perpendicular (at 90°) to the direction of energy transfer is called a

_____ wave. Examples of these waves are the _____ on the

surface of water, and _____ waves, such as light.

A wave that oscillates parallel to the direction of energy transfer is called a _____ wave.

An example of this kind of wave is a _____ wave produced by a loudspeaker.

Mechanical waves need a _____ to travel through.

B A student attaches a rope to a door handle and pulls it tight.

a Describe how she can make a **transverse** wave on the rope.

_____

_____

b Explain why she cannot make a **longitudinal** wave on the rope.

_____

_____

c Write down what is transferred by **both** transverse and longitudinal waves.

_____

d Here are some diagrams of seismic (earthquake) waves. The arrow shows the direction of motion of the waves in the ground.

Explain which wave is transverse.

_____

_____

The diagram of the longitudinal wave shows compressions and rarefactions. Explain the difference between a compression and a rarefaction.

_____

_____

Explain why seismic waves are mechanical.

_____

_____

P12.2 The properties of waves

A Fill in the gaps to complete the sentences.

The amplitude of a wave is the _____ displacement of a point on the wave from its undisturbed

position. This could be the height of a wave _____ , or the height of a wave _____

The wavelength of a wave is the distance from a point on a wave to the _____ point on the next

wave. This could be from one wave _____ to the next wave _____ .

You can calculate the period and speed of a wave using these equations:

$$\text{period} (_____) = \frac{\overline{\rule{4cm}{0pt}}}{\rule{4cm}{0pt}}$$

$$\text{speed} (_____) = \rule{10cm}{0pt}$$

[*You need to remember these equations.*]

B A musical instrument makes a note with a frequency of 200 Hz.

Calculate the period of the sound wave. Give the unit.

period = _____

C a A sound wave has a wavelength of 0.50 m and a frequency of 660 Hz.

Calculate the speed of the wave. Give the unit.

speed = _____

b Write down the wavelength of the wave if the frequency is doubled. _____

c A seismic wave has a speed of 4 km/s and a wavelength of 70 m.

Calculate the frequency.

frequency = _____ Hz

D A student writes some sentences about the properties of electromagnetic waves.

> *The distance from one peak to the next peak is the wavelength. Frequency is the number of waves per second. The un*
> *of frequency is seconds. The unit of wavelength is metres. The distance from a peak to a trough is the amplitude.*

a Underline the **correct** sentences.

b Rewrite the **incorrect** sentences.

_____

_____

_____

_____

_____

_____

P12.3 Reflection and refraction

A Fill in the gaps to complete the sentences.

Plane waves are reflected from a straight barrier at the _____ angle as the incident waves. This
is because their _____ and wavelength do not change.

Plane waves crossing a boundary between two different materials are _____ unless they cross
the barrier at _____ incidence.

At the boundary of two different materials, _____ occurs, because the speed and wavelength
of the waves change at the boundary.

At a boundary between two different materials, waves can be _____ or _____ .

B a Complete the diagrams to show what happens when waves in a ripple tank are reflected (diagram **X**), and
when they are refracted (diagram **Y**).

reflection

X

refraction

Y

b On diagram **X** label the angle of incidence and the angle of refraction.

c Describe and explain what happens to the wavelength of the waves that are refracted.

_____

_____

d Here is another diagram of waves crossing a boundary in a ripple tank.

Compare the waves in diagram **Y** and the waves in diagram **Z**. Explain whether or not diagram **Z** shows
refraction.

Z

_____

_____

_____

_____

Suggest why you can see the bottom of a swimming pool, but the bottom of a deep ocean is completely dark.

_____

_____

P12.4 More about waves

A Fill in the gaps to complete the sentences.

You hear an echo when a sound wave _____ from a smooth, hard surface.

You can measure the speed of sound by measuring the _____ interval between seeing a short loud sound being made and hearing it. If you also measure the _____ you can use the equation:

$$\text{speed (\_\_\_\_)} = \frac{\rule{6cm}{0.4pt}}{\rule{6cm}{0.4pt}}$$

to find the speed of sound.

B a Define an echo.

_____

b Describe how to use two wooden blocks and a large building to measure the speed of sound.

_____

_____

_____

_____

_____

_____

_____

c A student stands a distance of 150 m from a wall and measures a time delay of 0.90 s between making a sound and hearing the echo.

Calculate the speed of sound.

Give your answer to the appropriate number of significant figures.

speed = _____ m/s

d Estimate the uncertainty in:

- the student's measurement of the distance. _____

- the student's measurement of the time. _____

e Use your estimates to describe the effect of these two uncertainties on the value of speed that you calculate in part **c**.

_____

_____

_____

_____

P12.5 Sound waves

A Fill in the gaps to complete the sentences.

The sound waves produced in _____ are rhythmic; they change smoothly with regularly _____

patterns. Sound waves which vary randomly, with no pattern in their frequency, are called _____.

Sound waves can be used to measure distances using the technique of _____ _____, in

which the wave travels from a transmitter to a surface and then _____ back to a receiver.

Our _____ can detect frequencies between 20 Hz and 20 kHz. Sound waves hit our _____

_____, which vibrates. These vibrations produce electrical signals in the inner ear, which are sent to the

_____.

When a sound wave passes from one material to another, the _____ and the _____ can

change but the _____ remains the same. Not all frequencies of sound waves can pass a boundary like

that between the air and the ear drum, which is why human hearing has a _____ _____.

B A sound wave passes from the air into a wall. Complete the table to show the changes in the properties of the wave.

	Frequency in Hz	Speed in m/s	Wavelength in m
In air	500	330	**a**
In wall	**b**	**c**	3.4

C A sound wave travels from a transmitter on the bottom of a ship to the
seabed and back to the receiver, as shown in the diagram. Sound waves
travel at 1500 m/s in seawater and the pulse takes 0.30 seconds to travel
from the transmitter to the receiver.

Calculate the depth of the water beneath the boat.

depth = _____ m

The density of the seawater increases slightly with depth. This causes an
increase in the speed of the sound wave.

Suggest how this increasing density might affect the depth reading calculated in part **a**.

_____

_____

During a hearing test, a signal generator is connected to a loudspeaker so that it can produce sound waves of
constant intensity but varying frequency.

Describe and explain how the sound heard would change as the frequency of the sound waves produced is gradually
increased from 0 Hz to 25 kHz.

NT Remember that the ear's sensitivity changes with frequency. It is at its most sensitive for sounds around 3000 Hz.

_____

_____

_____

_____

_____

P12.6 The uses of ultrasound

A Fill in the gaps to complete the sentences.

Ultrasound waves have a frequency above _____ and cannot be detected by our _____.

Ultrasound scanners used for medical applications make use of ultrasonic pulses to generate images of

_____. A pulse is generated by a _____ and the pulse is then _____

_____ at boundaries in the body. The _____ part of the pulse continues deeper into

the body but the _____ part of the pulse travels back to the transducer. Timing information from the

reflected parts of pulses allows the thickness of tissues within the body to be measured.

Ultrasound scanning devices can also be used to analyse materials in industry; for example, by finding _____

or flaws inside metal pipes.

B Complete the table to compare the use of X-ray imaging and ultrasound imaging, including one situation where each technique would be used.

	X-ray	Ultrasound
Example procedure		
Advantages		
Disadvantages		

C A student has compared ultrasound waves with X-rays incorrectly, as shown. Write out a corrected version of their work.

_____

_____

_____

_____

_____

_____

_____

_____

> Ultrasound waves are transverse waves
>
> that are part of the electromagnetic
>
> spectrum along with X-rays. We cannot see
>
> ultrasound because it has too high a
>
> frequency for us to detect. Because we
>
> cannot see them they cannot ionise us and
>
> cause harm.

D This chart was produced by an industrial ultrasound scanner when looking for flaws inside a thick metal pipe. Point A on the chart shows the reflection from the outer surface of the pipe wall and point B shows the reflection from the inner surface.
The speed of sound in the metal is 4600 m/s.

a Explain how the chart shows that there is a flaw in the pipe.

_____

_____

_____

b Calculate the thickness of the pipe wall.

thickness = _____ mm

P12.7 Seismic waves

A Fill in the gaps to complete the sentences.

The shock waves produced by an earthquake are called _____ _____. The two most

important types of these waves are the primary (P) waves, which are _____ waves, and the secondary

(S) waves, which are _____ .

The waves from an earthquake are detected by a _____ . Patterns in the waves which arrive have

revealed evidence about the _____ _____ of the Earth.

B The diagram below shows the paths of P- and S-waves produced by an earthquake.

Explain each of the following observations shown in the diagram.

a The path of the waves through the mantle is curved.

_____

_____

_____

b S-waves do not pass into the outer core.

_____

_____

c There is a 'shadow zone' where no S- or P-waves are detected.

_____

_____

_____

_____

C The planet Mars is thought to have a dense metallic core, a thick mantle, and a thin crust, but no liquid outer core. Mars is geologically inactive so there are no 'Mars-quakes'.

Suggest how the internal structure of Mars might be confirmed experimentally.

HINT Think about what could cause shock waves that could then be analysed.

_____

_____

_____

_____

_____

_____

P12 Practice questions

01.1 Describe the difference between mechanical waves and electromagnetic waves. [1 mark]

_____

_____

01.2 Compare the speed of mechanical waves with the speed of electromagnetic waves. [1 mark]

_____

_____

02 A sound wave underwater has a frequency of 1000 Hz and a wavelength of 1.5 m.

02.1 Calculate the speed of sound in water. [3 marks]

_____

_____

_____

02.2 Calculate the period of the wave. [3 marks]

_____

_____

_____

02.3 A fishing boat uses echo sounding to find the depth of a shoal of fish. It sends out a sound pulse from the bottom of the boat and an echo is received 0.12 s later. The speed of sound in seawater is 1500 m/s.

At what depth is the top of the shoal of fish? [2 marks]

_____

_____

03 A student makes plane waves in a ripple tank. She puts a barrier in the tank to turn the waves through an angle of 90°.

03.1 Draw the incoming waves and the barrier position that would achieve this. [2 marks]

03.2 Write what is happening to the wave. [1 mark]

_____

03.3 Describe **two** other things that can happen to waves when they interact with matter that do not involve a change in direction. [2 marks]

_____

_____

04 A group of students collect some data from an experiment to measure the speed of sound. They stand a long way from a wall and make a sound. They measure the distance as 200 m and the time as 1.3 s.

04.1 Describe how they measured the time in this experiment. [2 marks]

_____

_____

04.2 Use the data to calculate the speed of sound. Give your answer to 2 significant figures. [4 marks]

_____

_____

_____

04.3 Write down **one** improvement that the students could make to their experiment. [1 mark]

_____

_____

05 Geologists can use an explosion to produce a shock wave which passes into the ground to discover the structure of the rock formations directly below the explosion.

Explain how the geologists would obtain information about this structure and how they would be able to determine the thickness of different rock layers. [6 marks]

_____

_____

_____

_____

_____

_____

_____

_____

P12 Checklist

	Student Book	☺	☺	☹
I can describe what waves can be used for.	12.1			
I can describe what transverse waves are.	12.1			
I can write down what longitudinal waves are.	12.1			
I can write down which types of wave are transverse and which are longitudinal.	12.1			
I can define the amplitude, frequency, and wavelength of a wave mean.	12.2			
I can describe how the period of a wave is related to its frequency.	12.2			
I can write down the relationship between the speed, wavelength, and frequency of a wave.	12.2			
I can use the wave speed equation in calculations.	12.2			
I can draw the patterns of reflection and refraction of plane waves in a ripple tank.	12.3			
I can determine whether plane waves that cross a boundary between two different materials are refracted.	12.3			
I can explain reflection and refraction using the behaviour of waves.	12.3			
I can describe what can happen to a wave when it crosses a boundary between two different materials.	12.3			
I can write down what sound waves are.	12.4			
I can write down what echoes are.	12.4			
I can describe how to measure the speed of sound in air.	12.4			
I can describe the difference between musical notes and noise.	12.5			
I can describe and explain the frequency response of the ear.	12.5			
I can describe how ultrasound waves can be used to image and analyse internal structures in the body and industrial structures.	12.6			
I can compare the use of medical ultrasound to X-rays.	12.6			
I can describe the behaviour of seismic waves.	12.7			
I can explain how seismic waves can be used to obtain evidence of the structure of the Earth.	12.7			

P13.1 The electromagnetic spectrum

A Fill in the gaps to complete the sentences.

The waves of the electromagnetic spectrum are:

radio, _____ , _____ , _____ light, _____ , _____ - _____ , and gamma rays.

This list of waves is in order from the _____ to the _____ wavelength, and from the _____ to the

_____ frequency and energy.

The human eye can only detect _____ light, which has a range of wavelengths from _____ nm to

_____ nm.

Electromagnetic waves transfer energy from a _____ to an _____ .

You can use the wave equation:

_____ = _____

to calculate the frequency and wavelength of electromagnetic waves.

[*You need to remember this equation.*]

B Choose a correct electromagnetic wave to complete the sentences below. There may be more than one correct answer.

a _____ have a wavelength longer than microwaves.

b Ultraviolet waves transfer more energy than _____ .

c X-rays transfer less energy than _____ .

d The frequency of visible light is higher than the frequency of _____ .

e The speed of infrared waves is the same as the speed of _____ .

f _____ can have a wavelength that is bigger than 1 km.

C The wavelength of microwaves is 3 cm, and their frequency is 10 000 000 000 Hz.

Calculate the speed of microwaves. Include the unit.

wave speed = _____

D Calculate the smallest and the largest frequencies of waves that can be detected by the human eye. Use the wave speed that you calculated in activity **C**.

1 nm = 1×10^{-9}m

smallest frequency: _____   largest frequency: _____

P13.2 Light, infrared, microwaves, and radio waves

A Fill in the gaps to complete the sentences.

White light contains all the _____ of the visible spectrum.

Infrared radiation is used to carry _____ from remote control handsets and inside _____ fibres.

Your mobile phone uses _____ waves and _____ . Satellite TV uses _____ , and radio and TV

broadcasting uses _____ _____ .

Different types of electromagnetic radiation are hazardous in different ways. _____ waves and _____

can heat parts of the body, and _____ radiation can cause skin burns.

B Compare how infrared radiation is used in infrared cameras and in remote controls.

_____

_____

_____

_____

C **a** Describe how the human body detects infrared waves and light waves.

_____

b Remote controls use infrared waves. Describe how you can use a remote control to show that infrared waves can be reflected.

_____

_____

c Write down how you know that the walls of your house transmit microwaves and radio waves.

_____

_____

D The frequency of the microwaves used in a microwave oven is 2.45 GHz. The frequency of the microwaves used in a mobile phone is 0.1 GHz.

a Calculate the ratio of the frequency of waves used in the microwave oven to the frequency of waves used in the mobile phone.

ratio of the frequencies = _____

b The energy of an electromagnetic wave is proportional to its frequency. So the ratio of the frequencies is the same as the ratio of the energies.

Comment on the ratio that you calculated in part **a**, by describing how the microwaves in the microwave oven and the microwaves in the mobile phone are used.

_____

_____

_____

_____

_____

P13.3 Communications

A Fill in the gaps to complete the sentences.

We use radio waves of different frequencies for different purposes. This is because the wavelength and frequency

affect the _____ they travel, how much they _____ out, and how much

_____ they carry. Carrier waves are waves that are used to carry _____. They do this

by varying their _____.

We use _____ to transmit satellite television signals.

We need further _____ before we will know whether or not mobile phones are safe to use.

We send signals by _____ or _____ radiation down thin transparent fibres called optical fibres.

B a Sort the uses of radio waves and microwaves in order of those that need the shortest wavelength to those that need the longest wavelength.

Write the letters in the correct order below.

W local radio stations   **Y** international radio stations

X satellite TV and satellite phones   **Z** TV broadcasting

Correct order: _____

b Use the ideas of range, spreading out, and absorption to explain why:

i microwaves instead of radio waves are used for satellite communication.

_____

_____

ii national and local radio stations use radio waves of different wavelengths.

_____

_____

C a Describe how infrared waves are used for communication.

_____

b Explain why using infrared waves in this way is safer than using microwaves.

_____

D The diagram shows how a radio signal is produced from a sound (audio) signal.

a Write the correct letter next to each type of signal:

Carrier wave		Audio signal		Radio signal	

b Use the waves shown in the diagram to compare how a radio transmitter and a radio receiver work.

_____

_____

_____

_____

A Fill in the gaps to complete the sentences.

Ultraviolet waves have a _____ wavelength than visible light, and can harm the _____ and eyes.

X-rays are used by doctors in _____ to make X-ray images.

Gamma rays are used to kill harmful _____ in food, to _____ surgical equipment, and to kill _____ cells.

When _____ radiation travels through matter, it can make uncharged atoms charged.

X-rays and gamma rays can cause _____ to living tissue when they pass through it.

B a Explain why ultraviolet waves can cause skin cancer, but not cancers inside the body.

_____

_____

b Explain how X-rays or gamma rays can cause cancer.

_____

_____

_____

_____

_____

_____

c Describe the link between the wavelength of the radiation and the damage that it can do to DNA.

_____

_____

d Describe **one** way that damaging cells using ionising radiation is put to good use.

_____

_____

Explain how the ozone layer acts like sunscreen.

_____

_____

Compare X-rays and gamma rays by describing their wave properties, dangers, and method of production.

_____

_____

_____

_____

_____

_____

P13.5 X-rays in medicine

A Fill in the gaps to complete the sentences.

X-rays are used in hospitals to make X-ray images and to destroy _____ cells at or near the body surface.

X-rays are _____ radiation, so they can damage living tissue when they pass through it.

_____-energy X-rays are used for imaging, and _____-energy X-rays are used to kill cancer cells.

Bones and teeth _____ more X-rays passing through the body than soft tissue does.

B Describe **one** use in hospitals of:

a low-energy X-rays

_____

b high-energy X-rays

_____

c gamma rays.

_____

C The diagram shows an X-ray being taken of a broken bone.

a Suggest why the photographic film is in a light-proof wrapper.

_____

b Complete the diagram to show the paths of the X-rays.

Explain how the paths you have drawn produce the image on the photographic film.

_____

_____

_____

X-ray beam

skin

bone

limb

table

film in light-proof wrapper

c Suggest and explain which metal should be used to cover the parts of the body not being X-rayed.

_____

D Doctors use X-rays to diagnose medical problems. Each X-ray scan increases a person's annual dose of radiation.

The table shows radiation doses for two types of X-ray scan, and a typical person's average annual radiation dose.

	Dose in millisieverts
Chest X-ray scan	0.1
Whole-body X-ray scan	10
Average annual dose	2

a Calculate the number of chest X-rays that would give a patient the equivalent of their average annual dose of radiation.

_____

_____

b Suggest how the data in the table might influence whether or not a doctor decides to X-ray a patient.

_____

_____

_____

_____

P13 Practice questions

01   There are seven types of wave in the electromagnetic spectrum.

01.1 Write the waves in decreasing order of wavelength. [6 marks]

_____

_____

01.2 Describe the order of the waves in part **01.1** in terms of frequency. [1 mark]

_____

01.3 Write the wave that the human eye can detect.

_____ [1 mark]

02.1 Name **two** electrical devices used in the home that **emit** electromagnetic radiation. Next to each device, name the type of radiation that it emits. [4 marks]

1 _____

2 _____

02.2 Name **two** electrical devices used in the home that **absorb** electromagnetic radiation. Next to each device, name the type of radiation that it absorbs. [4 marks]

1 _____

2 _____

03   Radio waves and microwaves are used in communications.

03.1 The radio waves or microwaves are carrier waves. Describe what a carrier wave is. [1 mark]

_____

_____

3.2 Write down one advantage of using short wavelength radio waves instead of long wavelength radio waves. [1 mark]

_____

_____

_____

_____

3.3 Explain how you know from their uses that microwaves have a range of wavelengths. [3 marks]

_____

_____

_____

.4 Explain why it is difficult to do experiments to work out the size of the risk to human health of using mobile phones. [2 marks]

_____

_____

04   Look at the X-ray image in **Figure 1**, which was produced in a hospital.

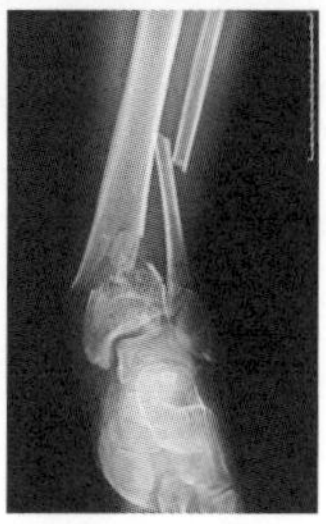

04.1 This radiation is ionising. Describe what 'ionising' means. [1 mark]

_____

_____

Figure 1

04.2 Explain why some parts of the image are black, and some are white. [3 marks]

_____

_____

04.3 Describe **two** precautions that the person making this image should take to reduce the risk of injury. Explain why the risk is reduced. [3 marks]

_____

_____

05   The frequency of a radio wave is 100 000 000 Hz, and it travels at 300 000 000 m/s. Calculate the wavelength of the radio wave. [3 marks]

_____

06   Doctors can use gamma rays to produce images of internal organs, such as the kidneys as shown in **Figure 2**.

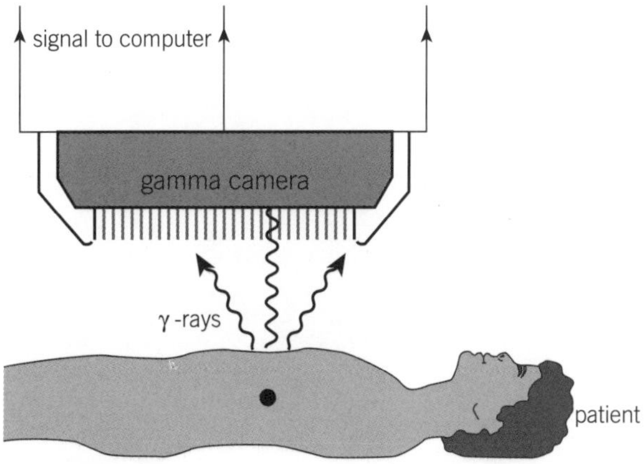

signal to computer

gamma camera

γ -rays

patient

Figure 2

06.1 Explain why you cannot use X-rays to produce an image of the kidneys. [1 mark]

_____

_____

06.2 Suggest why the precautions that are taken to reduce the risk of injury to a patient having an X-ray cannot be used for this patient. [2 marks]

_____

_____

P13 Checklist

	Student Book	☺	☺	☹
I can write down the parts of the electromagnetic spectrum.	13.1			
I can write down the range of wavelengths within the electromagnetic spectrum that the human eye can detect.	13.1			
I can describe how energy is transferred by electromagnetic waves.	13.1			
I can calculate the frequency or wavelength of electromagnetic waves.	13.1			
I can describe the nature of white light.	13.2			
I can name some uses of infrared radiation, microwaves, and radio waves.	13.2			
I can write down what mobile phone radiation is.	13.2			
I can explain why these types of electromagnetic radiation are hazardous.	13.2			
I can explain why radio waves of different frequencies are used for different purposes.	13.3			
I can write down which waves are used for satellite TV.	13.3			
I can describe how to decide whether or not mobile phones are safe to use.	13.3			
I can describe how optical fibres are used in communications.	13.3			
I can describe what a carrier wave is.	13.3			
I can describe the differences between ultraviolet and visible light.	13.4			
I can name some uses of X-rays and gamma rays.	13.4			
I can write down what ionising radiation is.	13.4			
I can explain why ultraviolet waves, X-rays, and gamma rays are dangerous.	13.4			
I can describe what X-rays are used for in hospitals.	13.5			
I can explain why X-rays are dangerous.	13.5			
I can write down which parts absorb X-rays when they pass through the body.	13.5			
I can explain the difference between the uses of low- and high-energy X-rays in hospitals.	13.5			

A Fill in the gaps to complete the sentences.

The law of reflection states that for any ray of light, the angle of _____ is equal to the angle of

_____. Both of these angles are measured from the _____, which is a line drawn

_____ to the point at which the ray meets the mirror.

The image formed by a plane mirror is _____ and it appears at the _____

_____ behind the mirror as the object is in front of it.

Surfaces which are very smooth cause _____ _____. This means that parallel rays of light

from the same point on an object are reflected in the same direction, allowing us to see an image. Rougher surfaces

produce _____ _____, which does not produce an image because parallel rays hitting the

surface are reflected off in many different directions.

B Draw rays on the diagram to show how the image of a point object (such as the tip of a pin) can be seen in a plane mirror.

HINT Always use a ruler when drawing ray diagrams.

image
•

point object
•

C A student investigated the law of reflection by shining a narrow beam of light at a plane mirror and measuring the angle of incidence and angle of reflection. Their results are shown in the table.

Angle of incidence in degrees	30	35	40	45	50	55
Angle of reflection in degrees	32	34	41	45	48	54

What instrument was used to measure the angles in
this experiment? _____

What was the resolution of the measuring instrument in **a**? _____

What is the range of the angles of incidence used in the experiment? _____

What type of error does the data show? _____

How could the errors in this experiment be reduced?

_____

_____

Reflection of waves can be modelled by rays or through wavefronts.

scribe how the law of reflection can be explained using the wavefront model. You may draw a diagram on a
parate sheet of paper to support your explanation.

_____

_____

_____

_____

_____

P14.2 Refraction of light

A Fill in the gaps to complete the sentences.

When a ray of light passes from one material to another it can be _____ and change direction. This is

caused by a change of _____ of the light wave.

When light moves from a less optically dense material into an optically denser material its speed _____ .

This will cause a ray to bend _____ the normal unless it is travelling _____ to the boundary,

in which case it will not change _____ .

B A student has been asked to investigate the refraction of light when it passes from air into a Perspex block, to see if there is a relationship between the angle of incidence and the angle of refraction.

Describe how the student should carry out the experiment. Include a diagram.

_____

_____

_____

_____

_____

_____

_____

_____

_____

_____

C A diver is standing on the side of a pool.

Complete the ray paths shown, from an object on the bottom of the pool into the diver's eye, to show why the pool appears shallower than it really is. Explain your diagram.

HINT You'll need to show how the rays refract and then extend virtual rays back to find where the object appears to be.

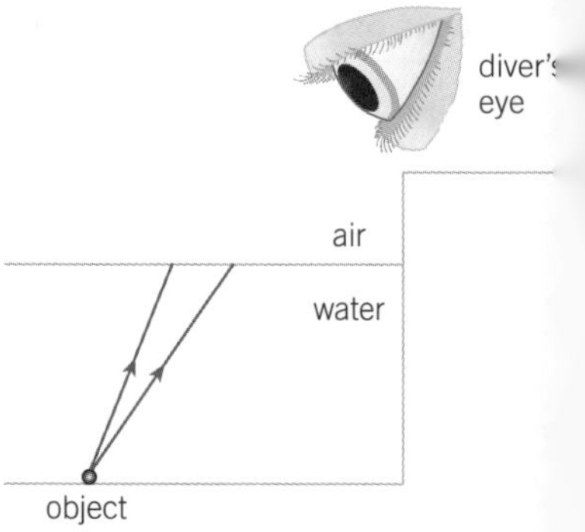

_____

_____

_____

D In some experiments a semi-circular glass block is used to investigate refraction as shown in the diagram. When an incident ray of white light reaches the back surface of the block it can split into a range of colours.

Suggest why this effect happens.

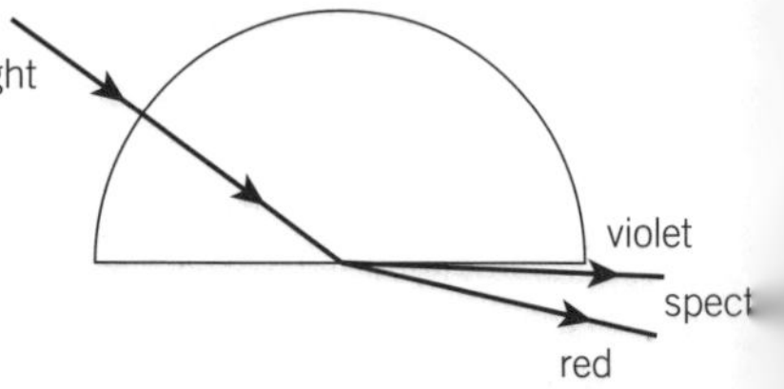

_____

_____

_____

_____

_____

P14.3 Light and colour

A Fill in the gaps to complete the sentences.

Objects that transmit all of the light incident on them are described as _____. Translucent materials

allow light to pass through but there is _____ and _____ of the light, which means we

cannot see objects clearly through them. Objects that transmit no light are described as _____.

B Beams of red, green, and blue light are made to overlap on a white screen.

a Colour in the diagram (or label it if you don't have colours) to show what is seen where the beams overlap.

b Describe and explain how the overlapping beams would appear if they were shone onto a red sheet of paper (with no other source of light present).

_____

_____

_____

C Different types of light source emit different colours of light.

a Describe how the light emitted by a laser differs from the light emitted by a filament lamp.

_____

_____

Why should protective goggles with green lenses be worn when operating a high intensity red laser?

_____

_____

The graph opposite shows the black body spectrum of electromagnetic radiation emitted by stars of different temperatures. The temperatures are given in the unit kelvin (K) rather than degrees Celsius (°C). The region for visible light is also shown.

e surface temperature of our Sun is 5800 K
5500 °C), that of the star Betelgeuse is
00 K (~3220 °C), and that of Rigel is 11 000 K
0 700 °C).

e the graph to explain what colour each of
se three stars appear in the night sky.

_____

_____

_____

_____

_____

_____

_____

_____

P14.4 Lenses

A Fill in the gaps to complete the sentences.

Lenses work by _____ light as it passes through them. Parallel rays of light that pass through a

_____ (or converging) lens are refracted towards the _____ _____ of the lens.

Parallel rays that pass through a _____ (diverging) lens are refracted so that they appear to have passed

through the _____ _____.

Convex lenses can form a range of different images. As the object gets _____ to a convex lens the image

gets _____ and further away.

The magnification produced by a lens can be found using the relationship:

$$\text{magnification} = \frac{\rule{3cm}{0.4pt}}{\rule{3cm}{0.4pt}}$$

B An 'IMAX' cinema projector uses a lens to project the image of a film cell onto a large screen. The film cell has a width of 69.6 mm and produces an image which is 40.0 m wide.

a Calculate the magnification required to produce this image.

_____

b The height of the film cell is 48.5 mm.

Calculate the height of the projected image.

_____

c Why does magnification have no unit?

_____

C Complete this pair of diagrams to show how a convex lens **a** and a concave lens **b** affect three parallel rays entering them.

Use the appropriate symbols to represent the two lenses and label the focal length in each case.

D When powerful lenses are used to observe objects there can be some distortion of the colours. There may appe to be 'fringes' of colours around the edges of bright objects.

Use your understanding of how white light is refracted to explain why this effect occurs, and suggest why it is more significant with highly curved lenses than with lenses of lower curvature.

_____

_____

_____

_____

_____

P14.5 Using lenses

A Fill in the gaps to complete the sentences.

Cameras use a _____ lens to form a _____ image on film or a pixel array. The lens can be

moved closer or further away from the film or pixel array to produce a _____ image; objects closer to the

camera need the lens to be moved _____ from the film.

Concave lenses cannot be used in cameras because they

always form _____ images.

B The diagram shows an object placed in front of a convex lens.

a Complete the diagram by drawing appropriate rays to show the image formed of the object by the lens.

b Give three properties of the image that has been formed.

_____

_____

C The diagram shows an object placed in front of a concave lens.

a Complete the diagram by drawing appropriate rays to show the image formed of the object by the lens.

b Give three properties of the image that has been formed.

_____

_____

_____

D To model the behaviour of the lens in an eye, a group of students constructed a lens using agar jelly. They made a rectangular block from the jelly and then used a flexible ruler to cut pieces from the front and back until it had the shape shown.

The lens was then placed on some stretchy fabric and a ray box was used to produce a set of rays that entered the lens.

What type of lens is shown? _____

Describe how the students could use their apparatus to investigate how the curvature of the lens affects its focal length.

_____

_____

_____

_____

_____

P14 Practice questions

01 You have been asked to design an experiment to investigate the refraction of a ray of light as it enters and leaves glass.

01.1 Suggest the equipment you would need for this experiment. [2 marks]

_____

_____

_____

01.2 On a separate sheet of paper, draw a plan diagram to show the apparatus in use. Mark in example incident, refracted, and emergent rays, and label the angle of incidence and angle of refraction. [2 marks]

01.3 Describe the method you would use in your experiment. [3 marks]

_____

_____

_____

_____

_____

_____

02 During an experiment to investigate the absorption of coloured light by coloured filters, a student used a ray box to produce a beam of white light which was detected by a light intensity meter. The meter measures the power of the light arriving (per square metre) at its sensor. The student recorded the reading of the meter with no filter and then with different coloured filters. The results are shown in **Table 1**.

Table 1

Filter	Light intensity in W/m²
none	0.63
red	0.21
green	0.23
blue	0.19
yellow	0.44
cyan	0.42

02.1 Write down the variables that need to be controlled in this experiment. [2 marks]

_____

_____

02.2 Explain why the detected light intensity decreases when the red filter is used. [2 marks]

_____

_____

02.3 The student concludes that the yellow and cyan filters allowed a greater range of wavelengths of light through than the other three filters. Justify the student's conclusion using the data. [1 mark]

_____

_____

02.4 Give an assumption that the student has made about the light meter. [1 mark]

_____

_____

03 An object is placed at the principal focus of a concave lens, as shown in **Figure 1**.

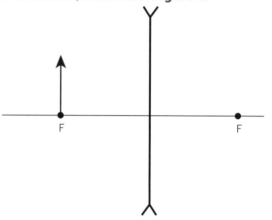

Figure 1

03.1 Complete the ray diagram to show how the lens produces an image of the object. [3 marks]

03.2 Describe the properties of the image produced by the lens. [3 marks]

_____

04 A group of students investigated the relationship between the magnification produced by a lens and the distance between the object and the lens. Their results are shown in **Table 2**.

Table 2

Object distance in cm	10.0	12.0	14.0	16.0	18.0	20.0
Magnification	2.0	1.7	1.4	1.3	1.1	1.0

04.1 Name the independent variable in this experiment. [1 mark]

_____

04.2 Name the dependent variable in this experiment. [1 mark]

_____

04.3 Write the equation used to calculate the 'magnification' of the lens. [1 mark]

_____

04.4 On a sheet of graph paper, plot a graph suitable for finding the relationship between the two variables. [3 marks]

04.5 Use your graph to suggest a relationship between the variables. [1 mark]

_____

P14 Checklist

	Student Book	☺	☺	☹
I can explain the difference between specular reflection and diffuse reflection.	14.1			
I can write the law of reflection and draw a ray diagram showing an example.	14.1			
I can explain reflection in terms of wave behaviour.	14.1			
I can draw a diagram showing how an image is formed in a plane mirror.	14.1			
I can describe the refraction of light as it passes from one material to another.	14.2			
I can describe how the refraction of light can be investigated.	14.2			
I can explain that refraction is caused by light having a different speed in different materials.	14.2			
I can explain that each colour of light has its own narrow wavelength and frequency band.	14.3			
I can describe the transmission or absorption of light by transparent, translucent, and opaque materials.	14.3			
I can explain the action of coloured filters.	14.3			
I can describe the reflection and absorption of coloured light by different coloured opaque objects.	14.3			
I can draw a ray diagram to show how light is refracted by a convex lens and by a concave lens.	14.4			
I can calculate the magnification produced by a lens.	14.4			
I can draw ray diagrams to find the position and properties of an image produced by a convex lens and by a concave lens.	14.5			
I can explain the difference between a real image and a virtual image.	14.1 14.5			

P15.1 Magnetic fields

A Fill in the gaps to complete the sentences.

When you bring two magnet poles together, they will _____ if the poles are the same, and

_____ if the poles are different.

The magnetic field lines of a bar magnet are in a direction from the _____ pole of the magnet to

the _____ pole of the magnet.

If you put a piece of magnetic material in a magnetic field, it will become an _____ magnet.

Permanent magnets are made out of _____ because it does not lose its magnetism easily.

A magnetic material such as _____ does lose its magnetism easily.

B Explain how you can use a permanent magnet to work out whether a bar of metal is magnetic or a permanent magnet.

_____

_____

C When you lift a paperclip out of a bowl of paperclips that have been used in magnetism experiments, it can attract other paperclips.

a Explain why new paperclips made of the same material do not do this.

_____

_____

b Suggest and explain the material that the paperclips are made of.

_____

_____

_____

D a Sketch the magnetic field lines around this bar magnet. Add arrows to the magnetic field lines to show the direction of the magnetic field.

N | S

b Explain what happens to the needle of a compass that is placed close to the magnet then moved a very long distance from the magnet.

_____

_____

_____

P15.2 Magnetic fields of electric currents

A Fill in the gaps to complete the sentences.

To draw the magnetic field pattern around a current-carrying wire, you need to draw _____ centred on the wire.

The magnetic field lines inside a solenoid are _____ and all in the same direction.

You can increase the strength of the magnetic field around a wire or in a solenoid by _____ the current. If you reverse the current, you _____ the direction of the magnetic field.

For a uniform magnetic field, the field lines are all _____ to each other.

B a Complete the diagram to show the shape and direction of the magnetic field around a current-carrying wire.
The current in the wire is in a direction into the paper.

b Describe how you would need to change your diagram if the current was reversed.

_____

C a Describe the difference between a solenoid and an electromagnet.

_____

_____

b Describe the difference between the magnetic field inside an electromagnet and the magnetic field outside the electromagnet.

_____

_____

D A student investigates how the current in an electromagnet affects its strength.

a Name **two** variables that the student will need to control in this experiment.

_____

b Sketch a graph of the mass of iron filings that the electromagnet picks up against current. Label the axes.

c Explain the shape of the graph.

_____

_____

d Explain **one** advantage and **one** disadvantage of using iron filings rather than paperclips in this experiment.

_____

_____

_____

P15.3 Electromagnets in devices

A Fill in the gaps to complete the sentences.

Electromagnets use an electric _____ to produce a controllable _____ _____.
They can be used in a wide range of electrical devices such as electric bells.

One such device is a circuit _____, which will automatically switch off a _____ if it becomes

too _____.

Another electromagnetic device is a _____, which is an electrical switch that can be used to switch on a

large current in another circuit.

B The diagram shows the circuit for an electric bell.

a On a separate sheet of paper, draw a flow chart to show the
operation of the bell. Start with 'The button is pressed …'

b The electromagnet has an iron core. Why is this used?

_____

_____

_____

_____

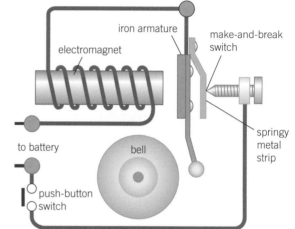

C A group of students investigated the factors that affect the strength of an electromagnet. They used a coil of wire
and a C-shaped core, as shown. They measured the weight that the electromagnet could support for a range of
current values and numbers of turns of wire on the coil. Their results are shown in the table.

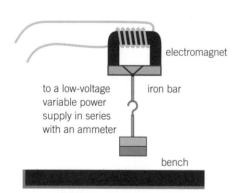

Current in A	Number of turns of wire around core	Maximum weight lifted in N		
		Test 1	Test 2	Test 3
0.5	20	2.0	1.0	1.5
0.7	20	2.0	2.0	2.5
0.9	20	2.5	2.0	2.5
0.5	30	2.5	3.5	2.0
0.7	30	2.5	3.0	3.0
0.9	30	3.5	3.0	3.0
0.5	40	3.0	3.5	3.5
0.7	40	4.0	5.0	3.5
0.9	40	4.5	3.5	4.0

a The students forgot to include the weight of the iron bar in their results.

Explain what type of error this mistake produced.

_____

_____

b Comment on the **precision** of the measurements in this experiment.

_____

_____

c What conclusions can be made about the factors affecting the strength of the electromagnet?

_____

_____

_____

P15.4 The motor effect

A Fill in the gaps to complete the sentences.

In the motor effect, increasing the current, the strength of the magnetic field, or the length of the conductor

will _____ the force. Reversing the direction of the current or the magnetic field will

_____ the direction of the force.

An electric motor has a _____ that turns when a current passes through it.

Magnetic _____ _____ is a measure of the strength of a magnetic field.

You can use the equation, with units in the brackets:

force (_____) = _____

to calculate the force on a current-carrying conductor at right angles to the lines of a magnetic field.

B A 0.2 m long wire carrying a current of 2.0 A is placed in a magnetic field where the flux density is 0.4 T.

a Describe how you need to place a wire in the magnetic field to produce the maximum force on the wire.

_____

b Calculate the force on the wire.

force = _____ N

c Calculate the current that would need to flow in the wire to produce a force of 0.05 N on the wire.

current = _____ A

C Look at the diagram. It shows a long wire carrying a current down through the centre of a piece of card. The direction of this current is into the paper.

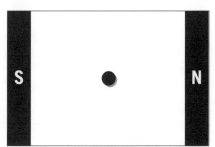

Use Fleming's left-hand rule to determine the force on the wire. Draw an arrow on the diagram to show the direction of the force.

Motors use this effect. Describe a simple electric motor.

_____

_____

Complete the table by describing the effect of making changes to a motor.

If you...	...then the motor will...
reverse the direction of the current in the coil	
decrease the current in the coil	
increase the strength of the magnets	

P15.5 The generator effect

A Fill in the gaps to complete the sentences.

When a _____ is moved inside a coil of wire, a _____ _____ is induced

across the ends of the coil. This is known as the _____ effect. If the coil is connected in a circuit then

a _____ will flow in the wire. The current induced in the wire will produce a magnetic field, which

_____ the motion of the magnet.

B A student investigates the generator effect by moving a magnet into and out of a coil connected to an ammeter, as shown.

Complete the table to show all the possible combinations of results.

Magnetic pole entering or leaving the coil	Pushed in or pulled out	Direction of current	Induced polarity of A	Magnet and coil
south pole	in	clockwise	south pole	repel
south pole	out	a	b	c
north pole	in	d	e	f
north pole	out	g	h	i

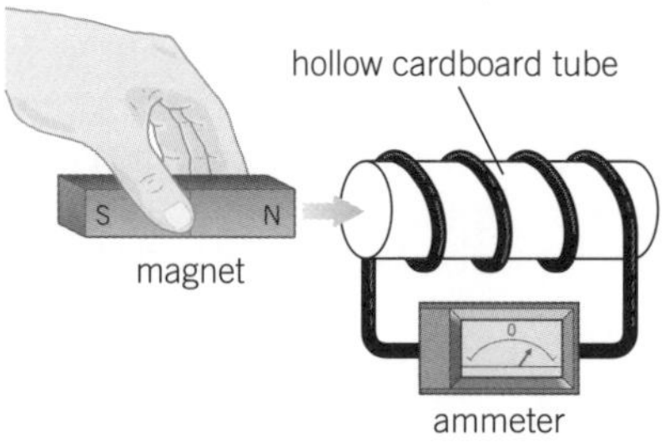

hollow cardboard tube

magnet

ammeter

C The diagram shows a wire, a pair of magnets, a metal frame, and a sensitive ammeter.

a Describe how this equipment can be used to demonstrate electromagnetic induction. Draw a diagram to aid your description.

_____

_____

_____

_____

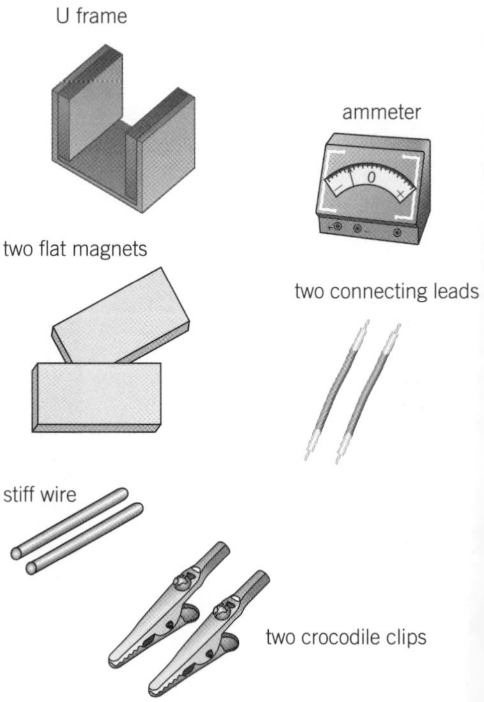

U frame

ammeter

two flat magnets

two connecting leads

stiff wire

two crocodile clips

b Outline how to demonstrate the effect of different factors on the size and direction of the induced voltage.

_____

_____

_____

_____

D On a separate sheet of paper, plan an experiment to determine how the **speed** of a magnet's movement into a solenoid affects the size of current induced.

P15.6 The alternating-current generator

A Fill in the gaps to complete the sentences.

An alternator is an _____ _____ generator. A coil of wire is rotated in a _____

_____ and this induces a potential difference in the wire. The _____ _____

switches direction each half turn of the coil.

A _____ is a direct current generator. This uses a _____–_____ commutator to

connect the coil to the external circuit. This causes the _____ of the current produced to stay the same

when the coil rotates.

A moving coil _____ uses the generator effect to produce an electrical signal. As _____

waves reach the coil they cause it to _____ in a magnetic field and this produces an _____

_____ , which has the same _____ as the sound wave.

Loudspeakers use the reverse effect; an _____ _____ will cause a coil to vibrate in a

magnetic field and this drives the speaker, producing a sound wave with the same _____ as the

electrical signal.

B The diagram shows the output cycle for an alternator and the some of the positions of the coil through the cycle.

a Match the positions of the coils to the correct times in the output cycle for an alternator, by drawing lines.

b Sketch a possible orientation for the coil at time t in the cycle.

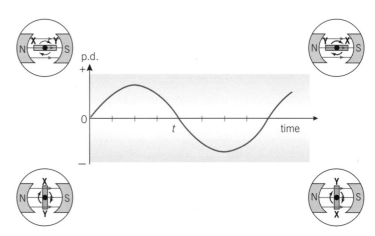

A direct current dynamo is connected to an oscilloscope to monitor its output. The coil is then rotated so that it induces a potential difference.

Sketch the output of a direct-current dynamo through one complete revolution of the coil on the axes below. Label the line A.

Add a second line to the same axes to represent the output from the same dynamo when it is rotated twice as quickly. Label the line B.

Describe in what way the trace would look different if an alternator were used instead of the dynamo.

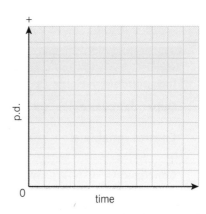

_____

_____

_____

P15.7 Transformers

A Fill in the gaps to complete the sentences.

A transformer is a device used to increase or decrease the _____ _____ of an electrical

power supply. It has two coils of wire, the _____ coil and the _____ coil, linked by

an _____ _____ . When there is an alternating current in the primary coil, a varying

_____ _____ is produced in the iron core. Changes to the flux density _____

a potential difference in the secondary coil.

B a Describe how a transformer is able to change the potential difference of an a.c. supply.

> **HINT** Make sure you describe changes in magnetic fields.

_____

_____

_____

_____

b Why will a transformer not work for a d.c. supply?

_____

_____

C Two groups of students investigated factors that affected the output voltage of a transformer. They used a varia
a.c. power supply (limited to a maximum output of 2.0 V), an iron core and coils of wire. Their results are shown
the two tables.

Group 1				Group 2			
Input voltage in V	Turns of wire on primary	Turns of wire on secondary	Output voltage in V	Input voltage in V	Turns of wire on primary	Turns of wire on secondary	Output voltage in V
0.20	20	60	0.59	0.50	60	30	0.24
0.40	20	60	0.79	0.50	60	60	0.49
0.80	20	60	1.58	0.50	60	90	0.74
1.00	20	60	1.98	0.50	60	120	0.98
1.20	20	60	2.48	0.50	60	150	1.48

a Complete the table below to show the variables for each group, and the conclusions that they can make fr
their results.

	Group 1	Group 2
Independent variable	i	v
Dependant variable	ii	vi
Control variable(s)	iii	vii
Conclusions	iv	viii

b What was the resolution of the a.c. voltmeter used by the groups? _____

c Suggest why the input potential difference was limited to a maximum of 2.0 V.

_____

_____

P15.8 Transformers in action

A Fill in the gaps to complete the sentences.

A transformer that increases the p.d. is called a _____–_____ transformer; this has _____ turns of wire on the secondary coil than on the primary coil. A transformer that decreases the p.d. is called a _____–_____ transformer; this has _____ turns of wire on the secondary coil compared to the primary coil.

The relationship between the primary and secondary p.d.s is given by the transformer equation:

$$\text{force} = \frac{\text{p.d. across primary coil}}{\underline{\hspace{3cm}}} = \frac{\text{number of turn on primary coil}}{\text{number of turns on secondary coil}} \text{ or } \frac{V_p}{V_s} = \frac{\underline{\hspace{0.5cm}}}{n_s}$$

B Complete this table showing the relationship between the potential difference and the number of turns on the coils in transformers.

Potential difference across primary coil in V	Number of turns on primary coil	Potential difference across secondary coil in V	Number of turns on secondary coil
230	500	a	40
110	275	12	b
30	c	5.0	50
d	250	10 200	3000

C The national grid uses transformers to step down from the very high p.d. used between pylons and the 230 V used in homes.

a Explain why the p.d. is made very high in the cables connecting the pylons.

HINT You can support your explanation using the relevant equation for electrical power.

_____

_____

_____

b Why is the p.d. lowered to 230 V for houses and flats?

_____

_____

c An engineer tested two different transformers to find their efficiency. The measurements are shown in the table below.

	Primary p.d. in V	Primary current in A	Secondary p.d. in V	Secondary current in A	% efficiency
transformer 1	12.0	1.22	48.7	0.30	
transformer 2	21.0	2.50	5.1	9.24	

Write the efficiency of each of the transformers in the table.

One of the transformers is faulty. Identify which one, and explain how the data show this.

_____

_____

P15 Practice questions

01 **Figure 1** shows a simple electric motor. The motor is spinning clockwise.

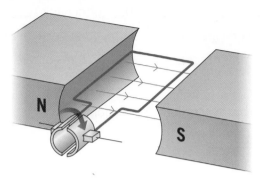

Figure 1

01.1 Draw two arrows on **Figure 1** to show the current flow in the long sides of the coil. [2 marks]

01.2 Write down what would happen to the motor if the current was reversed. [1 mark]

_____

01.3 Each side of the coil is 5 cm long, has a force on it of 0.005 N, and carries a current of 1.2 A.

Calculate the magnetic flux density. Give the unit. [3 marks]

magnetic flux density = _____

02 During an investigation of a transformer, students compared the potential difference (input) at the primary coil with the potential difference (output) at the secondary coil. Their results are plotted in **Figure 2**.

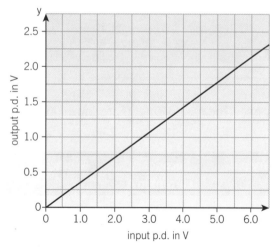

Figure 2

02.1 Determine whether the transformer was a step-up or step-down transformer.
Explain your answer. [1 mark]

_____

_____

02.2 The transformer had 66 turns of wire on the primary coil.
Calculate the number of turns on the secondary coil. [4 marks]

_____

_____

_____

02.3 The input coil of the transformer was connected to a 6.0 V power supply that provided a current of 0.5 A. The output coil was connected to a lamp.
Calculate the current in the lamp. [4 marks]

_____

_____

_____

_____

02.4 Write down any assumption you made in question **02.3**. [1 mark]

_____

03 **Figure 3** shows the simplified structure of a generator that is rotated with a period of 0.4 s.

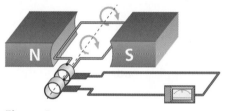

Figure 3

03.1 Predict whether this generator will produce an alternating or a direct potential difference.
Explain your answer. [1 mark]

_____

_____

_____

03.2 Sketch on the axes in **Figure 4** the output of this generator for one complete rotation of the coil. Label this line A. [3 marks]

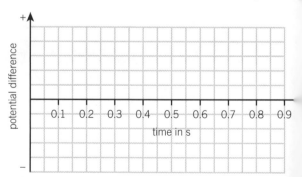

Figure 4

03.3 The same generator is rotated with a period of 0.8 s. Sketch this output on the same axes and label this line B. [2 mar

P15 Checklist

	Student Book	☺	☺	☹
I can write down the force rule for two magnetic poles near each other.	15.1			
I can describe the pattern of magnetic field lines around a bar magnet.	15.1			
I can write down what induced magnetism is.	15.1			
I can explain why steel, not iron, is used to make permanent magnets.	15.1			
I can describe the pattern of the magnetic field around a straight wire carrying a current.	15.2			
I can describe the pattern of the magnetic field in and around a solenoid.	15.2			
I can describe how the strength and direction of the magnetic field varies with position and current.	15.2			
I can write down what a uniform magnetic field is.	15.2			
I can write down what an electromagnet is.	15.2			
I can describe how electromagnets are used in a range of electrical devices including circuit breakers, bells, and relays.	15.3			
I can plan an investigation into the factors affecting the strength of an electromagnet.	15.3			
I can write down how to change the size and direction of the force on a current-carrying wire in a magnetic field.	15.4			
I can describe how a simple motor works.	15.4			
I can write down what magnetic flux density means.	15.4			
I can calculate the force on a current-carrying wire at right angles to the lines of a magnetic field.	15.4			
I can describe the processes of electromagnetic induction and the generator effect.	15.5			
I can describe the relationship between the movement of a magnet and the direction of the current it induces in a solenoid.	15.5			
I can describe the operation of an alternating current generator (alternator) and a direct current generator (dynamo).	15.6			
I can explain how electromagnetic induction and the motor effect are used in loudspeakers and moving coil microphones.	15.6			
I can label a diagram showing the structure of a transformer.	15.7			
I can explain how a transformer operates.	15.7			
I can use the transformer equation to perform a range of calculations.	15.8			
I can use the relationship between current and potential difference for the primary and secondary coils of a transformer.	15.8			
I can explain why transformers are used in the National Grid.	15.8			

P16.1 Formation of the Solar System

A Fill in the gaps to complete the sentences.

Stars form from clouds of _____ and dust which are attracted together by _____ forces.

As the particles become closer together, a _____ is formed, in which the temperature rises. When the

temperature in the centre reaches a high enough level, the _____ atoms begin to _____

_____ in a nuclear reaction. This process releases energy and the star begins to emit light.

For most of its life, a star is stable and is called a _____ _____ star. The force of

_____ compressing the star is balanced by the internal pressure produced by _____ of the

star pushing outwards.

B Complete this summary table to sort the objects found in our Solar System into order of size (1 being the largest). Then describe the key features of each type of object.

Size rank (1 to 5)	Object	Key features
	gas giant	
	asteroid	
	Sun	
	terrestrial (rocky) planet	
	moon	

C Our Sun is a main sequence star and so is stable in size and temperature. Describe fully the forces that maintain equilibrium in the Sun.

_____

_____

_____

_____

D Protostars are hot but do not produce radiation by nuclear fusion.

a Why are protostars hot?

_____

_____

b Suggest why it is difficult to detect protostars from telescopes on the surface of the Earth.

_____

_____

_____

P16.2 The life history of a star

A Fill in the gaps to complete the sentences.

As a main sequence star ages, it fuses _____ into helium in its _____. When the hydrogen nuclei are used up, the core collapses and the star expands, forming a _____ _____. The helium concentration in the core of the star has now increased enough for this to be _____ to form heavier elements.

Eventually all suitable fuels are exhausted and fusion processes in the core stop. A star that is about the same size as our Sun collapses into a _____ _____, which is very dense and hot. Eventually this will cool and become a _____ _____.

Very large stars become red _____ when their hydrogen runs out. When all of their nuclear fuel is exhausted they collapse catastrophically, producing an explosion that we call a _____. During the explosion a wide range of heavy elements are produced and scattered.

The remaining core of the very large star is compressed into an extremely dense _____ _____. This may collapse even further to form a _____ _____, whose gravity is so strong that not even _____ can escape.

B Our Sun is in the main sequence stage of its life and will remain there for several billion years.

On a separate sheet of paper, draw a large diagram showing the stages in the life cycle of our Sun from its origins to its final state. Include annotations to describe each stage and what is causing the change from one stage to the next.

HINT For example, name the process that causes heating, and mention which fuels are being used.

C 'All gold jewellery was made in a supernova explosion.'

Explain this statement scientifically and how the gold ended up on Earth.

_____

_____

_____

_____

The star Antares is a red supergiant with a mass 16 times that of the Sun. It can easily be seen with the naked eye. Within the next few hundred thousand years, Antares is likely to become a supernova.

Why will our Sun never become a supernova?

_____

_____

Suggest what any observers from Earth would see when Antares becomes a supernova.

_____

_____

P16.3 Planets, satellites, and orbits

A Fill in the gaps to complete the sentences.

An object moves in a circle when a _____ _____ acts on it. This force is always directed

towards the _____ of the circle and is _____ to the direction in which the object is moving

at any time. The speed of the object does not change, but the velocity changes because the object is undergoing a

constant _____ towards the centre.

The further an orbiting object is away from the body it orbits, the _____ it travels. This means that the

planets further away from the Sun take a _____ time to orbit it.

B The diagram shows two moons, X and Y, each orbiting the same planet in circular orbits. The moons are of equal masses, and this mass is very much less than that of the planet. The direction of travel of both moons is anticlockwise when viewed from this angle.

a Draw arrows on the diagram to show the forces acting on the moons. Show the relative size of the forces, as well as the direction. Label the arrows 'force'.

b Draw arrows to show the velocity of the moons at this instant. Show the relative size of the velocities, as well as the direction. Label the arrows 'velocity'.

c Explain, in terms of force and acceleration, why the moons follow circular paths.

_____

_____

_____

_____

C Geostationary communications satellites are placed 36 000 km above the equator. This large distance causes a 'signal delay' because electromagnetic waves travel at 300 000 km/s and so take a significant time to reach the satellite and return.

a Calculate the shortest possible time for a signal from the Earth to reach a geostationary satellite and return to Earth

_____

_____

b Explain why these communications satellites cannot be placed at a lower height in order to reduce signal delay.

_____

_____

_____

c The radius of the Earth is 6400 km. Calculate the speed at which a geostationary satellite travels, in km/h.

HINT You will need to work out the distance the satellite travels each day.

_____

_____

_____

P16.4 The expanding universe

A Fill in the gaps to complete the sentences.

If a star or a galaxy is moving _____ _____ the Earth, the _____ of the light

waves will be increased. This will mean that the light will look _____ than it would if the object were

not moving relative to the Earth. This change in wavelength is called _____–_____. The

_____ a galaxy is moving away from Earth, the greater the effect.

Edwin Hubble analysed the light emitted by a large number of galaxies and discovered that the _____

_____ the galaxy was, the _____ the red-shift. This provided evidence that the universe was

_____ .

B The diagram shows the absorption spectrum for a star which is **not** moving relative to Earth.

Draw and label two additional diagrams showing the spectral lines for identical stars which have light that is:

a red-shifted.

b blue-shifted.

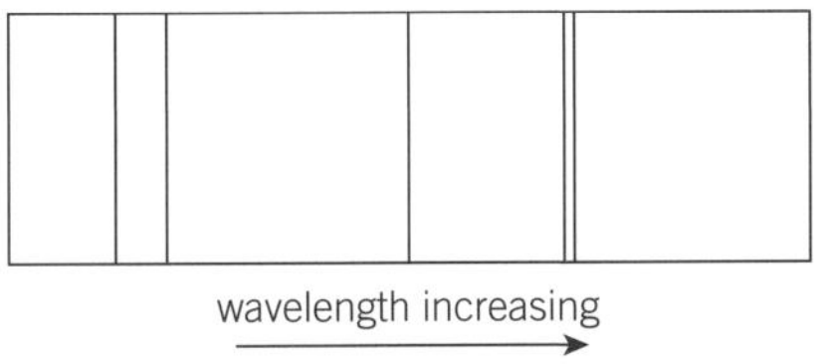

wavelength increasing

C Edwin Hubble's theory that the universe was expanding was initially rejected by many scientists.

a Suggest why the theory was initially rejected.

_____

_____

b Suggest why the theory eventually became accepted.

_____

_____

D Models are sometimes used to demonstrate complex ideas in science.

Design a way of demonstrating the expansion of the universe.

Explain how your model is similar to the expansion, and what the limitations are.

_____

_____

_____

_____

_____

_____

P16.5 The beginning and future of the Universe

A Fill in the gaps to complete the sentences.

The Big Bang theory is the model that states that the universe began as an unimaginably _____ ,
_____ , and _____ region, which _____ rapidly and cooled.

One of the most important pieces of evidence for this theory is the _____ _____
_____ _____ (CMBR), which is the remains of the radiation produced when the universe
was extremely hot. The wavelength of this radiation has _____ as the universe has _____ ,
so that what was once very _____ wavelength radiation now has a wavelength in the microwave region
of the _____ _____ .

B Sort these properties of the universe into the two columns in the table. Add any other properties that you know.

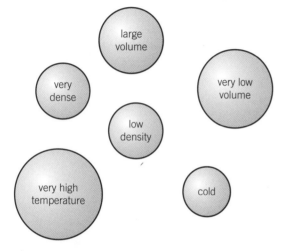

Properties of the current universe	Properties of the very early universe

C The table below shows the distance measurements and speeds of some galaxies that are travelling away from us.

Galaxy	Distance away in millions of light years (Mly)	Recession speed in km/s
1	20	440
2	34	748
3	72	1584
4	83	1826
5	120	2640

a Using the data in the table, plot a scatter graph on a sheet of graph paper, showing the relationship between the variables.

b Find the gradient of the graph. _____

c Use the graph to predict the recession speed of a galaxy that is 100 Mly from us.

_____

D The diagram shows two scenarios that were once thought possible for the universe in the distant future.

Recently, astronomers have discovered that the expansion of the universe is accelerating. Add a line to the diagram to show what will happen to the universe based on this new evidence.

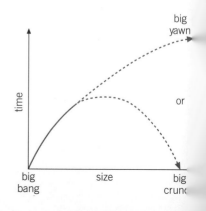

P16 Practice questions

01 Describe briefly how we believe the Solar System formed. [3 marks]

_____

_____

_____

02 Describe the life cycle of a star that is more than ten times as massive as the Sun. [6 marks]

_____

_____

_____

_____

_____

_____

03 **Table 1** shows the orbital radius and orbital period of some of the planets orbiting the Sun. The orbital radii are given relative to the orbital radius of the Earth.

Table 1

Object	Orbital radius relative to the Earth's	Orbital period in Earth years
Mercury	0.39	0.24
Venus	0.72	0.62
Earth	1	1
Mars	1.52	1.88
Jupiter	5.20	11.9

03.1 Plot a suitable graph (on a separate sheet of graph paper) to show any relationship between the orbital radius to the orbital period for these planets. [4 marks]

03.2 Describe the relationship between the orbital period and the orbital radius. [2 marks]

_____

_____

03.3 Estimate, using your graph, the orbital period for the asteroid 'Doris', which orbits the Sun with an orbital radius 3.11 times that of the Earth. [1 mark]

_____

04 The current model for the origin of the Universe is the Big Bang theory.

04.1 Describe the initial state of the universe, according to the Big Bang theory. [3 marks]

_____

_____

_____

04.2 Explain how observed red-shift of distant galaxies provides evidence that supports the Big Bang theory. [4 marks]

_____

_____

_____

_____

_____

_____

05 Analysis of the light from the galaxy Andromeda shows that its spectral lines are **blue-shifted**.

05.1 Explain what blue-shifted means and what this tells us about Andromeda. [2 marks]

_____

_____

05.2 In order to obtain information about the rotation of a galaxy, scientists can analyse the spectra of light from different parts of the galaxy. Simplified spectra for three parts of a galaxy, **X**, **Y**, and **Z**, are shown in **Figure 1**.

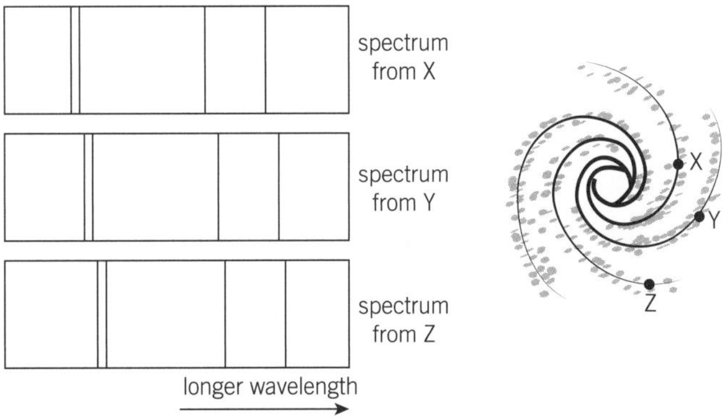

Figure 1

Explain how the three spectra provide evidence that the galaxy is rotating. [3 marks]

_____

_____

_____

_____

_____

_____

_____

P16 Checklist

	Student Book	☺	😐	☹
I can describe the formation of the Solar System from a nebula.	16.1			
I can describe how a star is formed and what provides its energy.	16.1			
I can explain why a star remains in a stable state (as a main sequence star), in terms of the forces acting.	16.1			
I can describe the life cycle of stars similar in size to our Sun.	16.2			
I can describe the life cycle of stars much larger than our Sun.	16.2			
I can explain the production of elements from fusion reactions, and describe where elements lighter than iron and those heavier than iron are produced.	16.2			
I can describe the forces involved when one object orbits another.	16.3			
I can describe the relationship between orbital speed and the radius of an orbit.	16.3			
I can explain what red-shift is.	16.4			
I can explain how red-shift is used to measure the movement of objects in the distant universe.	16.4			
I can explain how evidence from red-shift measurements supports the idea that the universe is expanding.	16.4			
I can describe evidence that supports the Big Bang theory, including the cosmic microwave background radiation.	16.5			
I can describe some features of the universe that have yet to be explained, such as 'dark matter'.	16.5			

Answers

P1.1

A store

heating, waves, electric current, a force

gravitational potential, kinetic

kinetic, surroundings, heating

B examples:

   a use a battery-powered appliance, e.g., a torch

   b lift an object, e.g., a book, onto a shelf

   c pull back / stretch an elastic band / spring

C at the beginning, there is energy in the chemical store of the food; this is transferred to the chemical store of your muscles when you eat; when you turn the handle, the energy in the chemical store decreases, and the energy in the thermal store of the surroundings increases; the transfer is made by forces when you turn the handle; by an electric current when you generate electricity; by heating and radiation when the wire inside the light bulb gets hot and emits light

P1.2

A created, destroyed, conservation, all

closed, energy

change

B it would swing forever and would always reach the same height; if there is no friction then the system is closed; there is no energy transfer in or out of the pendulum

C **a** the ball would bounce forever; it would always reach the same height;

   b the child would swing forever; the child would always reach the same height; the bungee jumper would bounce forever;

   c the bungee jumper would extend the bungee cord, bounce back up to the same height that she jumped from, and repeat

D **a** the system of the roller coaster itself is not closed, because of friction.

   b the system of the roller coaster, its surroundings, and its track is closed.

P1.3

A force, transferring

J, force (N) × distance moved in the direction of the force (m)

air resistance, friction, heat

work done (J) = force (N) × distance (m)

         = 15 (N) × 180 (m)

         = 2700 J

20 J, 3 J, 125 kJ, 1 kJ

independent variable: mass of sand

dependent variable: force on newton-meter

control variables: type of surface, tub, distance moved

the student needs to measure distance moved, mass of sand, and force needed; she needs to calculate the work done using the equation work = force × distance

she can work out the relationship by plotting a graph of mass against work done

P1.4

A increases, decreases

work, force, less, easier

J, mass (kg) × gravitational field strength (N/kg) × height (m)

B change in gravitational potential

energy = mass (kg) × gravitational field

       strength (N/kg) × change in

       height (m)

       = 30 kg × 10 N/kg × 1 m

       = 300 J

C 20 J, 0.16 J, 34 J, 0.01 J

D when the student pulls the tub across the floor, she is doing work against friction; when the student pulls the tub up the ramp, she is doing work against friction and against gravity; the work done pulling the tub up the ramp will be bigger, because she has to do work against gravity and against friction

P1.5

A mass, speed

J, 0.5 × mass (kg) × (speed (m/s))²

work, elastic

B **a** kinetic energy (J) = 0.5 × mass (kg) ×

            (speed (m/s))²

         = 0.5 x 0.05 (kg) ×

           (12.5 (m/s))²

         = 3.9 J

   b it is stationary

   c the ball is falling too fast to use a stopwatch, but using the light gates produces an accurate and precise result

C energy stored = 0.5 × spring constant (N/kg)

          × (extension (m))²

         = 0.5 × 145 N/m × (0.015)²

         = 0.0163 J

speed² = 0.0163 J / (0.5 × 0.05 kg)

      = 0.652 m²/s²

speed = 0.81 m/s

P1.6

A want

dissipation

wasted, surroundings, hotter/warmer

B **a** dissipating energy to surroundings due to friction / air resistance

   b dissipating energy to surroundings due to friction / electric current / sound waves

   c dissipating energy to surroundings due to outside of kettle being hot / electric current / sound waves

C **a** if you are travelling at a steady speed, the energy in the kinetic store does not increase

   b the energy is transferred to the thermal store of the surroundings because of friction, air resistance, and heating

   c wasted energy because the energy is transferred to the surroundings and does not increase the speed

      or

      useful energy because if no energy was being transferred from the chemical store of the fuel the car would slow down and stop

D when you use an electric heater, energy is dissipated, or transferred to the surroundings to heat the room by an electric current; the heating element in the heater gets hot, and useful energy is transferred by heating; the heater itself gets hot, and continues to heat the room, so there is no wasted energy, because the process that you want is that the room becomes warmer

P1.7

A $\dfrac{\text{useful output energy transfer (J)}}{\text{total input energy transfer (J)}}$

100, created

friction, heating, hotter, lubricating

B **a** efficiency

     $= \dfrac{\text{useful output energy transfer (J)}}{\text{total input energy transfer (J)}}$

     $= \dfrac{400 \text{ J}}{1000 \text{ J}}$

     = 0.4 or 40%

   b input energy transfer

     $= \dfrac{\text{useful output energy transfer}}{\text{efficiency}}$

     $= \dfrac{25 \text{ J}}{0.4}$

     = 62.5 J = 63 J

C energy is wasted by friction, sound, and heating; so to reduce friction and sound, lubricate the moving parts; and to reduce heating by electric current, use wires with a low resistance

D efficiency = useful energy / input energy, and at the start the input energy is the gravitational potential energy; so the student is correct if her use of the ball depends on it bouncing high, because if it does not then energy has been wasted when it bounces; but because there are many ways to use a ball that do not involve bounce height, the student's statement might not be correct

P1.8

A oil

electricity, cooking/heating, lighting, microwave

less

B a kettle is more efficient because you need less input energy to produce the same amount of useful energy than with an oven; this is because you would need to heat only a smaller kettle, not a whole oven, in addition to the water

C a **X**

  b **Y** requires more energy to be supplied per minute to produce the same amount of light, so there must be more wasted energy, so it is less efficient than **X**

  c **Y**

  d wasted energy = input energy – useful energy

    if the useful energy is the same but the input energy is larger, then more energy is wasted.

D power – a more powerful appliance will do a task in less time

efficiency – a more efficient appliance will waste less energy, so save money

P1.9

A rate

energy / work done (J)

time (s)

$\dfrac{\text{total power out (W)}}{\text{total power in (W)}} \times 100$

(W), total, (W), total, (W)

B power tells you the rate of energy transfer, and efficiency tells you the proportion of energy that is transferred usefully

a powerful device transfers energy quickly, but this might not be via the pathway that you want, so this might make it inefficient

C a useful power = $\dfrac{170\,000\,(\text{J})}{15\,(\text{s})}$

        = 11 333 W (11 000 W)

  b efficiency = $\dfrac{11\,000\,\text{W}}{20\,000\,\text{W}} \times 100$

        = 55%

  c wasted power = 20 000 W – 11 000 W

        = 9000 W

P1 Practice questions

01.1 energy is transferred from a gravitational potential store [1] to a kinetic store and a thermal store [1]

01.2 energy is transferred to the thermal store of the surroundings [1]

02.1 the scientist measured the time to boil the water, and looked at the power of the kettle [1]

energy supplied = power (W) × time (s) [1]

02.2 the amount of water [1]

02.3 efficiency

$= \dfrac{\text{useful energy transfer (J)}}{\text{total input energy transfer (J)}} \times 100\,[1]$

$= \dfrac{300\,000\,\text{J}}{400\,000\,\text{J}} \times 100\,[1]$

= 75% [1]

02.4 insulate the kettle / make it less noisy [1]

03.1 gravitational potential energy

= mass (kg) × gravitational field strength (N/kg) × change in height (m)

= 50 kg × 10 N/kg × 1.9 m [1]

= 950 J [1]

$E_k = 0.5 \times \text{mass} \times \text{speed}^2$ [1]

$\text{speed} = \sqrt{\left(2 \times \left(\dfrac{\text{energy}}{\text{mass}}\right)\right)}$

$= \sqrt{\left(2 \times \dfrac{950\,\text{J}}{50\,\text{kg}}\right)}$

= 6.2 m/s [1]

03.2 energy has been transferred to the thermal store of the surroundings [1]

04 example answer:

calculations of work done / gravitational potential energy:

work done = force × distance

          = weight × vertical height

          = mass × gravity × height

Empire State Building: gravitational potential energy = 10 × 70 kg × 10 N/kg × 86 × 3 m/floor

          = 1 800 000 J

The Shard: gravitational potential energy = 10 × 70 kg × 10 N/kg × 70 × 3 m/floor

          = 1 500 000 J [1 for value for ESB or Shard]

so the work done in moving people to the top of the Empire State Building is larger by a factor of 1.2 [1]

power of motor = $\dfrac{\text{energy}}{\text{time}}$

Empire State Building:

$\text{power} = \dfrac{1\,800\,000\,\text{J}}{55\,\text{s}}$

      = 33 000 W

The Shard: $\text{power} = \dfrac{1\,500\,000\,\text{J}}{60\,\text{s}}$

      = 25 000 W [1 for value for ESB or Shard]

so the power of the motor in the Empire State Building is larger by a factor of 1.32 [1]

$\text{efficiency} = \dfrac{\text{useful energy transfer}}{\text{total input energy}}$

$\text{total input energy} = \dfrac{\text{useful energy transfer}}{\text{efficiency}}$

wasted energy = total input energy – useful energy

Empire State Building:

$\text{total input energy} = \dfrac{1\,800\,000\,\text{J}}{0.85}$

      = 2 100 000 J

wasted energy = 2 100 000 J – 1 800 000 J

      = 300 000 J

The Shard:

$\text{total input energy} = \dfrac{1\,500\,000\,\text{J}}{0.9}$

      = 1 700 000 J

wasted energy = 1 700 000 J – 1 500 000 J

      = 200 000 J [1 for wasted energy for ESB or Shard]

so The Shard motor wastes two thirds of the energy that the Empire State Building motor does [1]

P2.1

A metals, non-metals

high

lower

B a **Y, Z, X**

  b the material with the lowest thermal conductivity will have the lowest rate of energy transfer through it, so its wax will melt last

  c use a temperature sensor at the end of the rod to measure the time more precisely / use an extended heat source so all rods are heated evenly / use one rod at a time so the heat source heats each rod the same amount

C the thermal conductivity of air must be lower than the thermal conductivity of the loft insulation material; using material that traps air lowers the overall thermal conductivity and makes the insulation more effective

P2.2

A electromagnetic spectrum, cannot, longer

higher, greater

continuous / wide range, intensity, wavelengths

B using an infrared camera / infrared sensor / as a rise in temperature, particularly with a blackened thermometer / by warmth on the skin

C absorbs all radiation that hits it, does not transmit or reflect any radiation, best possible emitter of radiation

D a curve **Y**

  b more radiation is emitted (in unit time) / intensity of radiation emitted is greater for object with curve Y; curve Y has a higher peak intensity but at a shorter wavelength; when the object is hotter (curve Y) it might appear blue/white–hot; when cooler (curve X) it is likely to be redder

P2.3

A absorb, emit (in either order), temperature, same rate

atmosphere, wavelength, longer

carbon dioxide, absorb, increase, greenhouse

B the can warms up quickly at first as it absorbs more infrared radiation than it emits; the rate of warming decreases as the can warms up and emits more radiation, while still absorbing the same amount as before; eventually, at a higher temperature (that of the surroundings), the can stops warming (its temperature becomes constant) as it absorbs and emits radiation at the same rate

C

	Surface of the Earth	Gases in the atmosphere
Daytime	Absorbs **more** radiation than it emits	Absorb **more** radiation than they emit
	Emits **longer** wavelength radiation than it absorbs from the Sun	Emit the **same** wavelength of radiation as they absorb from the Earth's surface
Night-time	Emits **more** radiation than it absorbs	Emit **more** radiation than they absorb

D short-wavelength infrared radiation from the Sun passes through the atmosphere; this radiation is absorbed at the surface of the Earth, warming it up; the warm surface re-emits radiation but at a longer wavelength; the longer-wavelength radiation is absorbed by greenhouses gases and re-emitted, partly back towards the Earth's surface; this occurs at night as well as in the daytime, which means the temperature of the Earth's surface does not fall too low at night and the average surface temperature is higher than if there were no greenhouse gases

P2.4

A 1 kg, 1
longer
energy, thermometer, mass

B **X**, **Y**, **Z**
energy needed depends on mass, specific heat capacity, and the change in temperature; **Z** is double **Z** because the specific heat capacity and mass are the same but the temperature difference is double for **Z**; **X** is smaller than **Z** because the mass is doubled and the temperature difference is also doubled, so the energy is quadrupled overall, but the specific heat capacity is $\frac{4200}{900}$ = 4.7 times smaller, so overall it is $\frac{4}{4.7}$ = 0.86 times smaller than **Z**

energy = power × time
energy needed to heat **Z** is $\frac{4}{(4200/900)} = \frac{4}{4.7}$
= 0.86, so the time taken to heat **X** would be 0.86 of the time taken to heat **Z**

a change in thermal energy (J)
= mass (kg) × specific heat capacity (J/kg °C) × change in temperature (°C)
= 0.25 kg × 4200 J/kg °C × 11.5 °C
= 12 075 J (12 000 J)

b it would take longer / twice as long / 30 minutes

2.5

oil, oil, wood
loft insulation, double glazing
two, cavity wall, thick / thicker, low / lower

B oil: stove, central heating system
coal or wood: stove, fire
gas: stove, central heating system, fire

C **a** foam that is pumped into the gap between two walls; low thermal conductivity
b loft insulation / thick carpets / double glazing; it traps air, which has a low thermal conductivity
c aluminium foil behind radiators; it reflects radiation away from the wall and does not trap air

D it would take $\frac{£2000}{£100 \text{ per year}}$ = 20 years before they start saving money with double glazing, but only $\frac{£175}{£25}$ = 7 years with loft insulation; with double glazing they would save: £100 × (30 − 20) years = £1000 with loft insulation they would save: £25 × (30 − 7) years = £575 so double glazing would be the better choice

P2 Practice questions

01.1 **Y** [1]
01.2 to prevent conduction (energy dissipation) through the base [1]
01.3 cups should have the same surface area (or volume) [1] so that a fair comparison can be made of the temperature drop due to radiation from the surface [1]
or cups should be made from the same material (e.g. all card) [1] so that the rate of conduction from the inside to the outside is the same [1]
02.1 to ensure that energy is transferred to the block and not to the surroundings [1]
02.2 specific heat capacity (J/kg °C)
$= \frac{45 \text{ J}}{1 \text{ kg} \times 20 \text{ °C}}$ [1]
= 2.3 (2.25) J/kg °C [1]
02.3 the measured value of the specific heat capacity is too high [1]
because the student needs to transfer more energy because it is heating the surroundings [1]
03.1 when the temperature difference doubles from 33 °C to 66 °C, [1] the thickness of insulation doubles from 38 mm to 76 mm [1]
$\left(\text{or } \frac{66}{33} = \frac{76}{38}\right)$
03.2 the materials used in modern sleeping bags have a lower thermal conductivity, [1] so the thickness needed can be less and still result in the same rate of transfer of energy [1]

P3.1

A coal, oil, gas
will
will not
biofuels, methane, ethanol
nuclear, more

B **a** biofuels / coal
b wood
C **a** a fuel produced from recently living plants, or animal waste
b it is renewable because you can produce more of it in a reasonable timescale
D **a** uranium atoms are unstable and can be split in two
b **i** 1 tonne of animal manure releases 12 MJ × 1000 = 12 000 MJ
mass of fissile uranium needed
$= \frac{12\,000 \text{ MJ}}{77\,000\,000 \text{ MJ/kg}} = 1.6 \times 10^{-4} \text{ kg}$
ii $\frac{1}{0.007}$ = 143 times as much uranium metal needed as fissile uranium
143 × 1.6 × 10⁻⁴ kg = 0.023 kg

P3.2

A turbine
wave
turbines, hydroelectric
tidal
environment / habitats
B **a** both rely on moving water to drive a turbine / generator to generate electricity
b both rely on moving air to drive a turbine / generator to generate electricity
C water behind a dam high up falls through turbines and generators to generate electricity
D **a** once the power station is built it costs very little to run
b a tidal barrage is very expensive to build compared with wave generators

P3.3

A generate, electricity, small, cheap, nothing
heat
mirrors, electricity
radioactive, water, steam, turbines
B all three use the light/radiation from the Sun; a solar heating panel uses radiation from the Sun to heat water, but a solar power tower and a solar cell panel generate electricity
C advantages: you can generate electricity in remote places; you do not need to be connected to a power station
disadvantages: solar cells convert less than 10% of solar radiation into electricity; solar panels work only on sunny days; solar cells are very expensive to buy; you need lots of solar cell panels to generate enough electricity to be useful

P3.4

A greenhouse, warming, acid rain
more, radioactive, expensive
do not, remote, animals, plants, expensive

B use carbon capture and storage to reduce effect of greenhouse gas carbon dioxide; remove sulfur to reduce the effect of acid rain

C wind
tidal
wind, solar
hydro
solar
wind, tidal, hydro, solar

D **a** a nuclear power station does not produce greenhouse gases / the energy produced from 1 kg of nuclear fuel is much greater than the energy from 1 kg of a fossil fuel

b there is less danger of an accident from a fossil fuel power station / radioactive waste lasts thousands of years

P3.5

A coal, pumped, expensive, decommission carbon capture, cheap, expensive, energy

B **a** the constant minimum amount of electricity that is needed

b by pumping water up into a reservoir at a hydroelectric power station

c solar power cannot provide the base load / cannot provide electricity at times of peak demand

C **a** capital costs are costs of building and decommissioning the station; running costs are daily costs of running the station

b will decrease as technology improves / use increases

D wind farm turbines are at the top of a pole so difficult and expensive to repair, so running costs are greater

P3 Practice questions

01.1 coal, oil, gas [1 for all three]

01.2 wind: uses air to turn a turbine, a turbine turns a generator [1]
waves: uses water to turn a turbine, a turbine turns a generator [1]
tides: uses water to turn a turbine, a turbine turns a generator, reliable resource [1]

02 the uranium in the fuel rods releases energy; [1] the core gets hot; [1] the coolant pumped through the core gets hot; [1] the hot coolant turns the water to steam; [1] the steam drives a turbine; [1] the turbine drives a generator, which produces electricity [1]

03.1 total percentage = percentage for oil + coal + gas
= 1% + 31% + 46% [1]
= 78% [1]

03.2 e.g., burning fossil fuels causes acid rain / produces greenhouse gases; [1] burning biofuels produces greenhouse gases but not acid rain; [1] greenhouse gases contribute to global warming; [1] sulfur can produce acid rain / sulfur dioxide [1]

03.3 one from: wind, waves, tidal, geothermal, hydroelectric, solar [1]

03.4 appropriate advantage, e.g., does not produce greenhouse gases, cheap to run [1]
appropriate disadvantage, e.g., expensive to install, unreliable [1]

04 **Sasha's reply:** I don't think we should, because they produce radioactive waste [1] and they are expensive to decommission. [1]
Dev's reply: I don't think we should, because they are expensive to install [1] and they can harm wildlife. [1]

05.1 a solar heating panel [1] or a solar cell panel [1]

05.2 total area of roofs in the UK = 25 000 000 × 140 m² = 3 500 000 000 m² [1]
output = 250 W/m² × 3 500 000 000 m² = 875 000 000 000 W [1]
percentage needed =
$$\frac{5\ 500\ 000\ 000\ W}{875\ 000\ 000\ 000\ W} \times 100\ [1] = 0.6\%\ [1]$$

05.3 suitable comment with reasoning, e.g., only a small proportion of houses needed, [1] but the calculation is based on the maximum output; [1] the cells would produce much less electricity than the maximum most of the time, [1] so the proportion of houses needed would be much bigger [1]

P4.1

A protons, neutrons (*in either order*), electrons
uncharged, ions, negative ion, positive ion
frictional, electrons, positively charged, negatively charged
electric field, lines of force, positive

B positive sphere: equally spaced radial lines with arrowheads pointing away from sphere
negative sphere: equally spaced radial lines with arrowheads pointing towards sphere

C frictional forces remove electrons from one object; electrons are transferred from one object, leaving it positively charged, to the other, making it negatively charged

D **a** the force increases in size as the objects become closer together

b the electric field between the object increases in strength. When they are very close together it may be strong enough to ionise the air, freeing electrons, which flow causing a spark

P4.2

A symbol, cells
rate
$$(A), \frac{charge\ (C)}{time\ (s)}$$

B diode

fuse

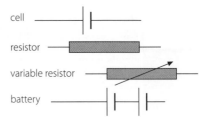

C **a** Charge is measured in coulombs/C. or Current is measured in amperes.

b Time is always measured in seconds.

c The current before a component is the same as the current after a component.

d Current is the rate of flow of charge/ charge flowing per second.

D 2 minutes = 120 seconds
$$current = \frac{15\ C}{120\ s} = 0.13\ A\ (0.125\ A)$$

P4.3

A energy, energy, volts
$$(V), \frac{energy\ (J)}{charge\ (C)}$$
$$(\Omega), \frac{potential\ difference\ (V)}{current\ (A)}$$
directly proportional, reverse

B **a** drawing of series circuit containing battery, lamp, and ammeter; voltmeter in parallel with lamp

b the ammeter is in series with the lamp because it measures the current through it; the voltmeter is in parallel with the lamp because it measures the difference in energy either side of it

c they would show a negative value of current

C $$charge = \frac{energy}{p.d.}$$
$$= \frac{200\ J}{12\ V} = 17\ C\ (16.7\ C)$$

D **a** $$I = \frac{V}{R}$$
$$= \frac{12}{30} = 0.4\ A$$
$$Q = I\ t,\ so\ t = \frac{Q}{I}$$
$$= \frac{600}{0.4} = 1500\ s$$

b its temperature does not change / it obeys Ohm's law / it is an ohmic conductor

P4.4

A increases
low, high, forward
decreases, increases

B **a** component **Z**: the current is proportional to the p.d.

b component **X**: the ratio of p.d. to current is higher at higher p.d.s / gradient of graph decreases at higher p.d.

c a diode: it has a low resistance for positive p.d. after about 0.7 V but a very high resistance for negative p.d.

C   light-dependent resistor: dark, light
     thermistor: cold, hot

D   as the electrons move through the filament
     wire they collide with the ions / atoms, which
     vibrate more as the wire gets hotter; the
     increasing collisions make it harder for the
     electrons to move through the wire

P4.5

A   current, potential difference, adding
     add
     increases, less

B a   X – 0.2; Y – 0.2; Z – 0.2; cell – 3;
        bulb 1 – 1.5; bulb 2 – 1.5

   b   the current everywhere in a series circuit
        is the same; the potential differences
        across the bulbs add up to the potential
        difference across the cell; the bulbs are
        identical so the potential difference
        across each of them is the same

C   resistance of bulb 1 or bulb 2 = $\dfrac{1.5\,V}{0.2\,A}$ = 7.5 Ω

     total resistance of circuit = $\dfrac{3\,V}{0.2\,A}$ = 15 Ω,

     or 2 × 7.5 Ω = 15 Ω

D   the bulbs are not ohmic conductors / the
     resistance of the bulb is not constant /
     increases with temperature

P4.6

A   potential difference, current, currents
     smaller
     (A) $\dfrac{\text{p.d. (V)}}{\text{resistance (Ω)}}$
     decreases, increases

   a   X – 0.2; Y – 0.2; Z – 0.4; cell – 9; bulb 1 – 9;
        bulb 2 – 9

   b   the current at Y will be the same as
        the current at X because the bulbs are
        identical and the potential difference
        across them is the same; the current at Z
        is the sum of the currents at X and Y; the
        potential difference across each bulb is
        the same as that across the cell

     resistance of bulb 1 or bulb 2 = $\dfrac{9\,V}{0.2\,A}$ = 45 Ω

     total resistance of circuit = $\dfrac{9\,V}{0.4\,A}$ = 22.5 Ω

     increase the p.d. of the cell / add another cell

Practice questions

1   they are charged oppositely / one is
     positive and one is negative [1]

2   the electric field strength increases as the
     rods become closer together [1] and so the
     force between the rods increases [1]
     close one switch, if all the bulbs go off it is in
     series, if only one goes off it is in parallel [1]
     10 Ω + 15 Ω = 25 Ω [1]

02.3   current = $\dfrac{\text{p.d.}}{\text{resistance}}$

        = $\dfrac{12\,V}{15\,Ω}$ and $\dfrac{12\,V}{10\,Ω}$

        = 0.8 A [1] and 1.2 A [1]

02.4   total current = 0.8 A + 1.2 A
        = 2 A [1]

        resistance = $\dfrac{\text{p.d.}}{\text{current}}$ [1]

        = $\dfrac{12\,V}{2\,A}$ = 6 Ω [1]

03.1   current (A) = $\dfrac{\text{charge (C)}}{\text{time (s)}}$ [1]

        = $\dfrac{20\,C}{40\,s}$ = 0.5 A [1]

03.2   the current flowing through a conductor is
        proportional to the p.d. across it [1] as long
        as the temperature stays constant [1]

03.3   resistance (Ω) = $\dfrac{\text{p.d. (V)}}{\text{current (A)}}$ [1]

        = $\dfrac{9\,V}{0.5\,A}$ = 18 Ω [1]

03.4   doubling the p.d. doubles the energy per
        charge (W = QV) [1]
        and also doubles the current $\left(I = \dfrac{V}{R}\right)$ [1]
        so twice as much charge flows per second
        and each charge transfers twice as much
        energy, so the energy per second is
        multiplied by 4 [1]

04.1   as the light level changes, the resistance of
        the LDR changes, [1] so the p.d across the
        LDR changes; [1] the voltmeter measures
        the p.d. across R_1, which is the p.d. of the
        cell minus the p.d. across the LDR, so that
        also changes [1]

04.2   example answer:
        in the light:
        total resistance = 100 Ω + 500 Ω = 600 Ω [1]
        current = $\dfrac{\text{p.d.}}{\text{resistance}}$

        = $\dfrac{6\,V}{600\,Ω}$ = 0.01 A [1]

        p.d. across R_2 = current × resistance
        = 0.01 A × 500 Ω
        = 5 V [1]
        in the dark:
        total resistance = 100 Ω + 500 000 Ω
        = 500 100 Ω
        current = $\dfrac{\text{p.d.}}{\text{resistance}}$

        = $\dfrac{6\,V}{500\,100\,Ω}$

        = 0.000012 A [1]
        p.d. across R_2 = current × resistance
        = 0.000 012 A × 500 Ω
        = 0.006 V [1]
        in the light, most of the p.d. is across the
        resistor; in the dark, most of the p.d. is
        across the LDR [1]

P5.1

A   one, reverses
     –230V, +230V, zero / 0
     network
     maximum, zero, period (for one cycle)
     Hz, $\dfrac{1}{\text{period (s)}}$

B   d.c. – straight horizontal line; a.c. – goes up
     and down about 0V

C a   325 V

   b   find the time for one cycle, then use the

        equation: frequency = $\dfrac{1}{\text{period}}$

   c   period = 0.02 s, f = $\dfrac{1}{\text{period}}$ = $\dfrac{1}{0.02\,s}$ = 50 Hz

   d   live, the p.d. on the graph varies between
        positive and negative values, but the
        neutral wire is 0V

   e   the value of 230V is the effective voltage
        because the p.d. varies / it is only at the
        peak voltage at 2 points in the cycle

P5.2

A   plastic, insulator
     copper, insulating
     brown, blue, green, yellow
     longest / centre, casing

B a   live, **brown**, carries the current to make
        an appliance work, **230**
        neutral, blue, **completes the circuit to
        make the appliance work, 0**
        earth, **green/yellow, safety /
        connected to earth to prevent you
        getting a shock**, 0

   b   similarity: both plastic / insulators
        difference: wire insulation is soft / flexible,
        but plug casing is stiff / rigid

C a   if you touch a case that is live / connected
        to the live wire then a current will flow
        through you

   b   if there is a fault the fuse melts and breaks
        the circuit; the current flows through the
        earth wire and not through you

   c   any appliance with a plastic case, e.g.
        hairdryer

   d   nothing / it would not work; there is no
        potential difference between the earth
        and neutral wires

P5.3

A   energy
     (J), power (W) × time (s)
     (W), potential difference (V) × current (A)
     (A), $\dfrac{\text{power (W)}}{\text{p.d. (V)}}$

B a   power is the rate of transfer of energy /
        energy transferred per second

   b   the bigger the power rating, the bigger
        the fuse needed; electrical power =
        V × I, so if p.d. is the same, bigger power
        means bigger current

C   15 kW = 15 000 W
     2.5 hours = 9000 s

energy transferred = 15 000 W × 9000 s
= 140 000 000 J (135 000 000 J)

D **a** current = $\frac{1000\,W}{230\,V}$

= 4.35 A (= 4.4 A)

b 5 A, a smaller value fuse would melt, and a higher value fuse would not protect the appliance

E resistance = $\frac{P}{I^2}$

= $\frac{350\,W}{(1.5\,A)^2}$

= 160 Ω (156 Ω)

P5.4

A (C), current (A) × time (s)
(J), p.d. (V) × charge (C)
heat up
energy, energy

B the electrons collide with the vibrating atoms / ions in the wire and transfer energy to them, so they vibrate more, so the wire heats up

C **a** 4 mA = 0.004 A
charge = 0.004 A × 0.1 s = 0.0004 C

b energy transferred = 300 000 C × 230 V
= 69 000 000 J

D a very small amount of energy is **dissipated** in the wires in the circuit, so the energy transferred to the components is slightly less than the energy transferred by the battery

P5.5

A energy
(J), power (W) × time (s)
(J), efficiency × energy supplied (J)
(W), efficiency × power supplied (W)

B **a** power = 230 V × 15 A
= 3450 W = 3500 W to 2 significant figures

b time

C **a** 30 minutes = 1800 s
energy transferred = 2000 W × 1800 s
= 3 600 000 J

b 70% = 0.7 as a decimal fraction
4000 kJ = 4 000 000 J
useful energy = 0.7 × 4 000 000 J
= 2 800 000 J

c efficiency = $\frac{useful\ energy}{total\ energy\ transferred}$ × 100

= $\frac{2\,800\,000\ J}{3\,600\,000\ J}$ × 100

= 78%

P5 Practice questions

01.1 **A**: green/yellow; **B**: brown; **C**: blue [all correct – 2, one correct – 1]

01.2 **A** [1]

01.3 **B** and **C** [1]

01.4 National Grid [1]

02 hard plastic, **casing, rigid insulator** [1]
flexible plastic, **insulation for wire, flexible insulator** [1]

copper, **wire, conductor** [1]

03 current = $\frac{power}{p.d.}$ [1]

= $\frac{1100\,W}{230\,V}$ [1]

= 4.78 A (= 4.8 A) [1]
so she needs a 5 A fuse [1]

04.1 2 min = 120 s
energy transferred = power × time [1]
= 800 W × 120 s [1]
= 96 000 J [1]

04.2 time = 6 min = 360 s
charge = current × time [1]
= 5.2 A × 360 s [1]
= 1872 C = 1900 C (to 2 s.f.) [1]

04.3 time = 24 × 60 × 60 = 86 400 s [1]
energy transferred = power × time
= 420 W × 86 400 s [1]
= 36 288 000 J
= 36 000 000 J (to 2 s.f.) [1]

05.1 time = 4 × 2 ms = 8 ms [1]
8 ms = 0.008 s [1]

frequency = $\frac{1}{period}$ [1]

= $\frac{1}{0.008\ s}$

= 125 Hz [1]

05.2 the peak p.d. is 15 V, but mains is 325 V / much higher [1]
the frequency is 125 Hz, but mains frequency is 50 Hz [1]

06 3 MJ = 3 000 000 J = useful energy transferred [1]
in 1990, energy per cycle = 2.7 kWh
2.7 kWh = 2.7 kW × 1000 (W/kW) × 3600 (s/h)
= 9 720 000 J [1]

efficiency = $\frac{useful\ energy}{total\ energy\ transferred}$ × 100

= $\frac{3\,000\,000\ J}{9\,720\,000\ J}$ × 100

= **30.8%** [1]
in 2010, energy per cycle = 1.4 kWh
1.4 kWh = 1.4 kW × 1000 (W/kW) × 3600 (s/h)
= 5 040 000 J [1]

efficiency = $\frac{3\,000\,000\ J}{5\,040\,000\ J}$ × 100

= **59.5%** [1]
the efficiency of dishwashers has nearly doubled in 20 years [1]

P6.1

A mass, volume, kg/m³
kg/m³, $\frac{mass\ (kg)}{volume\ (m^3)}$
density, volume, mass, density
mass, volume
less than

B density = $\frac{55\ kg}{0.07\ m^3}$ = 786 kg/m³

C an object floats if its density is less than the density of water; the ship has a much larger mass, but also a larger volume than the pebble; the ship's density is less than that of water (the large amount of air inside the ship

reduces the total density of the ship), but the density of the pebble is greater than the density of water, so the pebble sinks

D measure the mass of each object with a digital balance; measure the volume of the stone cube using a ruler; put the modelling clay into a known volume of water in a measuring cylinder; observe the volume increase; this gives the volume of the modelling clay

E mass of **X** = density of **X** × volume of **X**
= 1.5 g/cm³ × 10 cm³
= 15 g

volume of **Y** with this mass = $\frac{mass}{density}$

= $\frac{15\ g}{5\ g/cm^3}$ = 3 cm³

P6.2

A gas, liquid, solid
solid, gas,
mass

B in both arrangements, the particles are touching; density is the mass per unit volume; for a given mass, the volumes will be similar, and so will the densities

C **a**

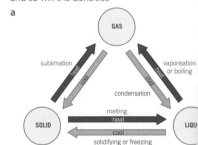

b the particles have more kinetic energy, because they are moving faster, and more potential energy because they are slightly further apart

D **a** it decreases

b the mass of water in the air + the mass of water in the bowl = the original mass of water in the bowl

c no new substances are formed

P6.3

A melts, freezes, boils, condenses,
horizontal
boiling, vaporisation

B This process happens at the boiling point of the liquid – *boiling*
The mass does not change – *boiling, evaporation*
The particles escape only from the surface the liquid – *boiling, evaporation*
This process happens at or below the boiling point of the liquid – *evaporation*

C **a** dotted line: melting point
first curved section: solid
horizontal section: solid + liquid
second curved section: liquid

b a mirror image of the graph in part **a**, with the line starting on the y-axis where it ends on the graph in part a;

horizontal line should be in the same
place on the temperature axis
label 'freezing point', instead of 'melting
point', on the temperature axis

4

ncreases
ttraction
inetic, potential
olliding
he kinetic energy of particles in a gas; the
nergy of vibration of the particles in a solid;
he gravitational potential energy of the
particles in a liquid
particles repeatedly collide with the surface of
he container

the kinetic energy of the particles in the
liquid increases, but the kinetic energy of
the particles in the solid decreases; there
is no change to the potential energy of
the particles in the solid or liquid

if a substance is melting or boiling /
vaporising, the energy will break the
bonds between the particles but not
increase the temperature; the internal
energy increases because the potential
energy increases, but the kinetic energy,
and so the temperature, does not increase

5

energy, temperature
kg, temperature
J), mass (kg) × specific latent heat (J/kg)
melt, boil
atent heat is the energy needed to change
he state of a substance; specific latent heat is
he energy to change 1 kg of the substance;
atent heat is measured in J; specific latent
heat is measured in J/kg
334 kJ/kg = 334 000 J/kg
hermal energy for melting ice =
    334 000 J/kg × 0.03 kg = 10 020 J
when you heat a substance and it changes
tate, you increase the potential energy but
not its kinetic energy; this requires more
energy per kilogram for a liquid to a gas
han for a solid to a liquid because you are
completely breaking the bonds between
particles

6

pressure
ncreases, more, increases
andom
Brownian motion / observing smoke
particles that you can see being moved by air
molecules that you cannot see
f the temperature is higher, the molecules are
moving faster, so they collide more often with
he walls of the container; so the gas exerts a
bigger force on the walls of the container as
he gas is heated

the mass of gas / volume of the
container; if either changed, the pressure

change would be due to more / fewer
particles, or fewer / more collisions
between the gas particles and the
container

b it would flatten off, or curve downwards,
because the number of gas particles
would decrease due to the leak, so the
pressure would be less

P6.7

A pressure, temperature (*in either order*)
compressed, expand
pressure, volume (*in either order*), temperature,
Boyle's law
work, temperature

B pressure is caused by the collisions of the
gas particles with the cylinder walls; as the
volume decreases, the rate of collisions with
the walls increases so the pressure inside the
cylinder increases

C **a** 0.4 m³

b 66 667 Pa or 66.7 kPa

c 0.125 m³

D **a** as the pump is used, work is done on
the air inside it (the force causing the
compression works against the pressure
of the air); this causes an increase in
the internal energy of the air and so
has a heating effect; if the compression
happens quickly there is no time for the
gas to cool by energy transfer to the
surroundings

b as the gas is released it expands into
the surrounding air so it is doing work
(against the external air pressure); this
causes a decrease in its internal energy
which has a cooling effect on the gas
and the can; the gas is forced out rapidly
so there is no time for energy transfer to
equalise the temperature

P6 Practice questions

01 energy to change the state of a material [1]

02.1 freezing is the process of particles moving
into a fixed pattern, with bonds forming
between them; [1] melting is the process
of particles moving from a fixed pattern
into an irregular pattern, with bonds
breaking / becoming weaker between
them [1]

02.2 vaporisation is the process of particles
changing from a liquid to a gas (bonds
breaking totally) at temperatures below
the boiling point; [1] boiling only occurs at
the boiling point [1]

03.1 the volume of the balloon will increase / it
will expand [1]

03.2 use of pressure × volume = constant; [1]
5.33 m³ [1]

03.3 **one** from: the temperature of the gas
remains constant; [1] the mass of gas stays
constant (no gas escapes) [1]

04.1 70 °C [1]

04.2 9 mins [1]

04.3 0 mins [1]

04.4 it is increasing [1] because the potential
energy is increasing as bonds are broken,
but the kinetic energy does not change
because the temperature does not
change [1]

05.1 **D** before **B**, [1] **B** before **C**, [1] **C** before **A**, [1]
A before **E** [1]

05.2 if the student does not collect all the water
from the melting of the ice, the mass
measured will be less than it should be [1]

specific latent heat = $\frac{\text{energy}}{\text{mass}}$ [1]

so if the mass is smaller, then the specific
latent heat will be bigger [1]

06 mass = 2 g = 0.002 kg
thermal energy for a change of state
= 0.002 kg × 334 000 J/kg
= 668 J [1]
temperature change = 20 °C [1]
change in thermal energy
= 0.002 kg × 4200 J/kg °C × 20 °C
= 168 J [1]
total energy = 668 J + 168 J
        = 836 J = 840 J [1]

P7.1

A unstable, stable
alpha, beta, gamma
random

B example: throwing a die, or tossing a coin;
you cannot predict the number / whether it
will be heads or tails

C alpha, α, **nucleus**
gamma, γ, **nucleus**
beta, β, **nucleus**

D **a** the rock is emitting waves or particles,
which are detected by the Geiger counter

b put a piece of paper between the sample
and the Geiger counter, and if the count
rate goes down the source is emitting
alpha radiation

c the atoms in a sample that produces a
reading are unstable / emitting radiation,
but those in a sample that does not
produce a reading are not

P7.2

A alpha, large
plum pudding
massive / small, positively

B **a** 2 lines with angle θ > 90°

b most alpha particles went through, so
most of the atom was empty space; a
few came back, so there is a very small,
dense, positively charged nucleus at the
centre of the atom, which repels the
positive alpha particles

C in both models there is a small, dense, positively
charged nucleus in the centre of the atom;
in Rutherford's model, the electrons orbit the
nucleus, but in Bohr's model, the electrons
can only orbit at certain distances, which are
called energy levels / shells

P7.3

A same, different, same, different
two / 2, two / 2, four / 4, two / 2
neutron, proton, electron, does not change, one / 1

B a $^{14}_{6}\text{X}$ $^{12}_{6}\text{X}$

   b isotopes have the same number of protons and different numbers of neutrons; the bottom number is the number of protons, so the two isotopes are the ones with the same bottom number

C in alpha decay, a nucleus loses two protons and two neutrons; in beta decay, the number of nucleons stays the same, but the number of protons increases by one, and the number of neutrons decreases by one

D $^{226}_{88}\text{Ra} \rightarrow\ ^{222}_{86}\text{Ra} +\ ^{4}_{2}\text{He}$

$^{218}_{84}\text{Po} \rightarrow\ ^{218}_{85}\text{At} +\ ^{0}_{-1}\text{e}$

E in both cases, an uncharged particle / wave is emitted, and the type of element does not change; in gamma emission, an electromagnetic wave is emitted, and the mass does not change; in neutron emission, a particle is emitted and the mass decreases

P7.4

A paper, aluminium, lead
a few cm, about 1 m, infinite
2 / two, 2 / two, fast, electron, electromagnetic
most, least
ionise, damage

B set up the Geiger counter so that is detecting radiation from the sample; put a sheet of paper between the counter and the sample: if the reading goes down, the sample is emitting alpha; put a sheet of aluminium between the counter and the sample: if the reading goes down, the sample is emitting beta; if there is no change with aluminium, the sample is emitting gamma

C a

It has an infinite range in air	γ	It consists of a fast moving electron	β
It is moderately ionising	β	It is the most ionising	α
It has a range of about 1 m in air	β	It has a range of a few cm in air	α
It consists of two protons and two neutrons	α	It consists of electromagnetic radiation	γ

   b it is the least ionising – γ

D irradiation means that the source of radiation was outside the strawberries; the strawberries do not become radioactive; eating them will not put radioactive material in the body, so will not cause cancer

P7.5

A halve, decreases, halve, 2^n

B count rate is the reading measured with a Geiger counter; activity is the number of decays per second

C Half-life is the time for the number of unstable nuclei to halve.
Half-life is the time for the activity to halve.

D a 6 days

   b initial activity = 80 counts/s

after 3 half-lives $= \dfrac{80}{2^3} = 10$ counts/s

   c 5 counts/s after 4 half-lives, which is 24 days
suitable method, e.g.:
counts: 80 – 40 – 20 – 10 – 5 means you need to halve 80 four times

   d the ratio of net decline $= \dfrac{1}{2^6} = \dfrac{1}{64}$

P7.6

A diagnose
radioactive tracer, gamma, gamma camera, short, stable isotope
radiotherapy, narrow beam, radioactive

B they shield themselves when possible from the radiation, for example behind a lead screen; they wear personal radiation monitors to record how much radiation they have been exposed to over a period of time

C **three** from: radon gas, cosmic rays, food and drink, radiation emitted from the ground

D a the count rate increases as the tracer enters the kidney but does not decrease afterwards, showing that the tracer is not leaving the kidney

   b the tracer would decay too rapidly; the count rate would decrease too quickly whilst inside the kidney, making it look as if the tracer was leaving the kidney

P7.7

A nucleus, neutron, gamma rays / radiation, neutrons, chain reaction
fuel rods, moderator, control rods, absorb

B a *control rods* – absorb some of the emitted neutrons to slow the reaction rate until it is stable
fuel rods – contain the fissionable fuel isotopes (such as uranium-235)
moderator – slows neutrons until they are the correct speed to cause more fission reactions
coolant – cools the reactor and heats water to produce high-pressure steam

   b *steel shell* – to withstand the high temperature and high pressure of the core
concrete shield – to absorb some of the gamma radiation emitted by the core

C a a series of fission reactions caused when the neutrons released from one fission go on to cause more fission reactions

when absorbed by a fissionable nuc which will release even more neutro and so on

   b without control by the control rods the neutrons from each fission woul on to cause further fissions, repeate and continuously, so a huge amoun energy would be released rapidly in explosion

P7.8

A small nuclei, larger
Sun, stars

B a overall, the mass of the particles invo decreases; the mass lost is converted energy

   b $^{3}_{2}\text{He} +\ ^{3}_{2}\text{He} \rightarrow\ ^{4}_{2}\text{He} + 2\text{p}$

C a *advantages*: much greater supply of fu (water) available, no radioactive waste produced, helium produced (harmles
disadvantages: very expensive to construct, complex to operate, very high temperatures are hard to reach maintain, workers have less experien how to operate them

   b it has not been possible to create the correct conditions (very high temperature and pressure) for suffici long periods of time

P7.9

A background radiation, radon, alpha parti
radioactive waste, half-life, activity / radioactivity
Chernobyl, radioactive material

B **three** from:
medical applications: it is difficult to redu exposure from these, as medical professi will only use radioactive sources for diagr or treatment when there is no alternative
air travel: reduce flights taken
nuclear power: avoid living near nuclear power or waste reprocessing plants
nuclear weapons: press for governments agree on bans

C a cause very high level of ionisation damaging cells in small area

   b cause ionisation damaging cells

   c high

   d medium

   e can penetrate skin and cause ionisat of cells beneath

   f cause lower level of ionisation over w area

P7 Practice questions

01.1 an alpha particle is a helium nucleus / protons and two neutrons; a beta part is a fast-moving electron; a gamma ray an electromagnetic wave [1]
alpha is absorbed by paper; beta by aluminium; gamma by lead and concrete [1]

alpha travels a few cm; beta about 1 m; gamma has an infinite range [1]

01.2 when radiation ionises, it loses energy; [1] alpha is very ionising, so does not travel far because it loses a lot of energy, [1] but gamma hardly ionises so has a very large range [1]

02 **six** from: description of fuel rods; [1] example fuel (e.g. uranium-235); [1] fission process; [1] chain reaction; [1] function of moderator; [1] function of control rods; [1] heat exchanger between coolant and steam; [1] reactor containment [1]

03.1 alpha [1]

03.2 gamma [1]

03.3 beta [1]

03.4 beta or gamma [1]

04.1 the number of unstable nuclei [1]

04.2 initial activity = 2000 counts/min [1]
activity after 5 half-lives

$$= \frac{2000}{2^5} [1]$$

= 62.5 counts/min [1]

= 63 counts/min (cannot have half a count) [1]

05.1 ionising radiation can damage or kill cells [1]

05.2 the nucleus of technetium-101 has two more neutrons than the nucleus of technetium-99 [1]

05.3 $^{101}_{43}\text{Tc} \rightarrow {}^{101}_{44}\text{Ru} + {}^{0}_{-1}\beta$ [2]

05.4 the half-life of technetium-101 is too short / it would not emit enough radiation to detect / may not have reached the kidneys before it has decayed too much; [1] it emits beta radiation, which is ionising and could cause cancer; [1] beta radiation would be stopped by the body tissue and would not be detected by the camera outside the body [1]

P8.1

A distance
magnitude, direction, magnitude
direction, magnitude

B a e.g. temperature / distance; it has no direction

b because an arrow can show a direction

a 20 cm east

b 90 cm

suitable scale diagram with scale shown (e.g. 4 cm arrow upwards and 1 cm arrow to the left, scale 5 N/cm)

8.2

size, shape, stationary, newtons
contact
equal, opposite

a e.g. a football changes shape when it is headed

b e.g. a car accelerates when it is on the motorway

c e.g. a cyclist starts moving when she pedals

C contact forces are exerted when objects are in contact, e.g. friction; non-contact forces are exerted whether or not the objects are in contact, e.g. gravity

D a when two objects interact with each other, they exert equal and opposite forces on each other

b the forces acting are the force of the Earth on you, and the force of the chair on you, so both forces are acting on you, not on different objects.

c when you walk, you exert a force on the floor, and the floor exerts a force on you, so you move forward

d when the fuel burns, exhaust gases leave the bottom of the rocket; the pair of forces are the force of the gas on the rocket and the force of the rocket on the gas; when the force of the gas on the rocket upwards exceeds the force of the Earth on the rocket (weight), the rocket takes off

P8.3

A same
zero
bigger, zero
add, difference
free-body

B if the cyclists is moving at a constant speed then friction/air resistance balances the force from the cyclist, so the resultant force is zero

C a stationary, moving at a steady speed

b 7, 3, **4, to the left**
10, 20, **10, to the right**
80, 150, **70, to the right**

D a arrow pointing up; arrow pointing down; both arrows shown on the dot

b you are in equilibrium/at rest; the arrows are equal length but in opposite directions

P8.4

A force, turning, moment, force, distance, pivot
N m, force (N) × perpendicular distance from the line of action of force to the pivot (m)

B a

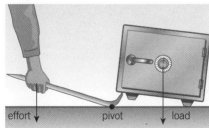

effort   pivot   load

b 100 N m

c 1000 N or 1.0 kN

C a 1.5

b 0.58

c 40

D sketch shows a greater distance between the object and a pivot (e.g. shoulder) when the object is at arm's length; explanation states that this causes a greater turning effect at the pivot (joint), which the body has to balance with a force (from the muscles)

P8.5

A multiplier, pivot
turning effect, low, large / high, high, smaller / lower

B a Y

b X

C a 3.01; 2.86; 2.94; 2.84

b 2.9(1)

c it will be larger, because the turning moment is the same for the axle and the wheel, so with a larger radius of wheel the effort force can be smaller to lift a particular load

P8.6

A point
centre
below
line

B the racing car is not as high so that its centre of mass is lower, so it is less likely to topple over when it goes round a corner at high speed

C circle with dot in the centre, rectangle with dot in the centre, triangle with dot in the centre

D a **a** – vertical arrow pointing down to the right of the pivot; **b** – vertical arrow pointing down on the pivot; **c** – vertical arrow pointing down to the left of the pivot; all arrows start at centre of mass

b to topple the lorry, the weight has to act to the left of the pivot; the centre of mass must be to the left of the pivot; so a wind will need to move the centre of mass by a big distance, so the wind needs to be very strong

P8.7

A equilibrium
principle, moments, clockwise moments, anticlockwise moments (*last two in either order*)

B a $W = 96$ N

b $F = 176$ N

c force F acts at a distance of 0 m from the pivot / through the pivot and its moment is 0

C a 8.30 N; 7.98 N; 7.68 N; 8.33 N

b 8.07 (8.1) N

P8.8

A scale
resultant
protractor
origin

B you use a parallelogram of forces when the forces are acting at an angle to each other, but not when they act in a single line

C a diagram with one arrow two-thirds the length of the other, and the angle between them = 30°

b 9.7 (10)

D a resultant drawn using the parallelogram of forces

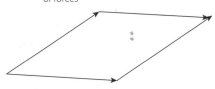

b i length of resultant increases; angle between resultant and tug A increases
ii the resultant would be the force of tug B

P8.9

A 90°
rectangle, diagonal
equilibrium
rest

B a 90°
b the magnitude of the normal force when you are sitting on the flat ground is bigger than the magnitude of the normal force when you are sitting on the hillside

C rectangle drawn; correct horizontal and vertical forces (8.6 N and 5 N)

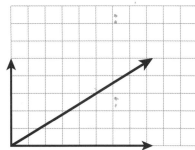

D a components drawn along the slope and perpendicular to the slope

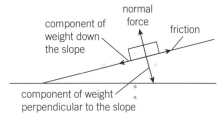

b angle of the ramp and weight of the block; then the student can draw a scale diagram to find the force down the slope, which is equal to the frictional force
c the height will be smaller; the frictional force is less, so the component of the weight down the slope will need to be much smaller

P8 Practice questions

01 the moment of a force has both magnitude and direction [1] whereas temperature only has magnitude / no direction [1]
02 friction, tension, air resistance [all correct – 2, 2 or 1 correct – 1]
03.1 → 3N; [1] 0N; [1] ← 1N [1]
03.2 box B; [1] there is zero resultant force [1]

03.3 accelerate to the right; [1] move to the left at 3 m/s; [1] move to the left and slow down [1]
04.1 the total of clockwise moments about any point / about the pivot must equal the total of anticlockwise moments about the same point; [1] there must be zero resultant force acting on the wheelbarrow [1]
04.2 calculation of moment due to soil = 360 N m; [1] calculation of force on handles = 327 N [1]
04.3 the moment decreases [1] because the perpendicular distance of the centre of mass from the pivot decreases [1]
05 they are the same [1]
06.1 it is below the suspension point [1]
06.2 dot with arrow downwards labelled 'weight' [1] and arrow up and to the right at 30° to vertical labelled 'tension'; [1] vertical component of tension drawn upwards; [1] scale used to produce answer: T = 57 N [1]

P9.1

A m/s, $\dfrac{\text{distance (m)}}{\text{time (s)}}$
stationary, steady / constant speed
gradient

B a speed = $\dfrac{11\ m}{2.7\ s}$ = 4.1 m/s
b steady / constant speed

C a distance travelled = 5.5 m/s × 15 s
= 83 m
b time = $\dfrac{70\ m}{5.5\ m/s}$ = 13 s

D in section **A**, the object is travelling at a steady speed; in section **B**, the object is stationary; the line is straight with a gradient; the line has zero gradient

in **A**, speed = $\dfrac{\text{distance}}{\text{time}}$
= $\dfrac{20\ m}{4\ s}$
= 5 m/s, constant speed
in **B**, speed = 0 m/s, constant speed

P9.2

A direction
vector, scalar
(m/s²), $\dfrac{\text{change in velocity (m/s)}}{\text{time (s)}}$
slows down
velocity

B a speed has magnitude only, velocity has magnitude and direction
b 10 m/s north, 38 mph south

C a speed = $\dfrac{\text{distance}}{\text{time}}$
= $2 \times \pi \times \dfrac{r}{t}$
= $2 \times 3.14 \times \dfrac{25\ m}{20\ s}$
= 7.9 m/s

b the velocity has a constant magnitude but the direction is constantly changing so it is accelerating towards the centre the circle
c the speed is the same, but the velocit are in opposite directions

D a change in velocity = 100 m/s – 0 m/s
= 100 m/s
acceleration = $\dfrac{100\ m/s}{30\ s}$
= 3.3 m/s²
b change in velocity = 140 m/s – 155 m/
= –15 m/s
acceleration = $\dfrac{-15\ m/s}{120\ s}$
= –0.125 m/s²

P9.3

A motion sensor, gradient, zero
positive gradient
negative gradient
distance travelled
B advantage: a motion sensor can plot the graph as the object is moving
disadvantage: it needs to be connected to computer at the time of analysis
C accelerating; decelerating; moving at a ste speed
D a acceleration = $\dfrac{(18\ m/s - 0\ m/s)}{15\ s}$
= 1.2 m/s²
b total distance travelled
= $\dfrac{1}{2}$ (18 m/s × 15 s) + (18 m/s × 30 s) +
$\dfrac{1}{2}$ (18 m/s ×
= 810 m
c the change in velocity is the same; the time to change is the same; so the acceleration is the same magnitude b negative (–1.2 m/s²)

P9.4

A gradient
gradient
area under
gradient, tangent
B a horizontal line on a distance–time graph means that the object is stationary; a horizontal line on a speed–time graph mea that the object is moving at a constant spe but if the speed is zero the object is statior
C zero, zero, positive
D a gradient drawn on graph; speed = 10
b gradient drawn on graph; speed = 8.5
c graph **B**; the speed is increasing at a steady rate

P9 Practice questions

01 7.4; [1] 0.24; [1] 26 [1]
02 acceleration = $\dfrac{\text{change in speed}}{\text{time}}$ [1]
= $\dfrac{0.5\ m/s}{0.05\ s}$ [1]
= 10 m/s² [1]

1000 m or 3000 m [1]

$$\text{speed} = \frac{\text{distance}}{\text{time}}$$

$$= \frac{2000\,\text{m}}{600\,\text{s}}\,[1]$$

$$= 3.3\,\text{m/s}\,[1]$$

using a stopwatch [1] and a trundle wheel [1]

A to **B**: $\text{acceleration} = \frac{\text{change in speed}}{\text{time}}$

$$= \frac{7\,\text{m/s}}{10\,\text{s}}\,[1]$$

$$= 0.7\,\text{m/s}^2\,[1]$$

between **B** and **C**: zero; [1] between **C** and **D**: acceleration is half / 0.35 m/s², [1] and negative / it is deceleration [1]
the cyclist's speed is changing so you cannot use distance = speed × time [1]

$\text{distance} = \frac{1}{2}\,(7\,\text{m/s} \times 10\,\text{s}) + (7\,\text{m/s} \times 20\,\text{s})$

$$+ \frac{1}{2}\,(7\,\text{m/s} \times 20\,\text{s})\,[1]$$

$$= 245\,\text{m}\,[1]$$

the time it takes to travel half the circle: [1] the acceleration is the change in velocity divided by the time; [1] the velocity changes by 10 m/s, so you need time to calculate acceleration [1]
tangent drawn; [1] values of displacement and time used from tangent [1]

$$\text{speed} = \frac{(60\,\text{m} - 0\,\text{m})}{(0.88\,\text{s} - 0.24\,\text{s})}$$

$$= 9.4\,\text{m/s}\,[1]$$

0.1

increase, mass
smaller
N, mass (kg) × acceleration (m/s²)
rest, constant / uniform
if the force acting on an object increases, so does the acceleration; if the mass of an object increases but the force stays constant, the acceleration will decrease
inertial mass is a measure of the resistance an object has when a force is exerted on it

a   mass = 105 g = 0.105 kg
    resultant force = 0.105 kg × 3.20 m/s²
    = 0.336 N
b   1.6 m/s²
c   the ball in part **b**; it has greater mass, so requires a bigger force to change its motion
d   double it; if the mass doubles, you need to double the force to produce the same acceleration

P10.2

A   force, matter
        10
        terminal
        frictional, zero
B a   mass is the quantity of matter, in kg, which is what bathroom scales show; weight is the force of gravity acting on a mass, in N, so the scales read mass not weight
       b   2 (N), 1.1 (kg), 0.053 (N)
C a   10 m/s²
       b   there are forces other than gravity acting on the stone, e.g. water resistance
       c   the velocity increases until it hits the water because the force of gravity is bigger than air resistance; when it hits the water, it slows down because of the force of the water on the stone; it reaches terminal velocity when the water resistance equals the weight
D   straight diagonal line (or line with slightly decreasing gradient) until it hits the water; decrease in velocity to much smaller value with vertical line with decreasing gradient, then horizontal line, then vertical line when it hits the bottom; an 'x' on the horizontal line

P10.3

A   driving
        thinking, braking
        braking, thinking
        N, mass (kg) × acceleration (m/s²)
B a   braking distance: the distance a car travels while the driver is applying the brakes; depends on speed, mass of the car, brakes (force, condition), road condition
            thinking distance: the distance the car travels while the driver is reacting (i.e. during the reaction time); depends on speed, tiredness, level of alcohol in blood, distractions
       b   e.g. if the lorry has a much slower speed than the car, but they have similar brakes / reaction times
C a   force = 1000 kg × 4 m/s²
            = 4000 N = 4 kN
       b   u = 30 m/s
            $\text{acceleration} = \frac{-u^2}{2s}$

            $$= \frac{-900\,\text{m}^2/\text{s}^2}{2 \times 120\,\text{m}}$$

            $$= -3.75\,\text{m/s}^2$$
            (a deceleration)
            yes, because the deceleration of magnitude 4 m/s² is greater than this
       c   if the acceleration is constant then the distance depends on the speed squared

P10.4

A   kg m/s, mass, kg, × velocity, m/s
        the same as, conservation
B   momentum = mass × velocity.
        if the mass of the lorry is twice that of the car it needs to have half the velocity to have the same momentum as the car
C   momentum = mass × velocity
            = 300 000 kg × 2 m/s
            = 600 000 kg m/s
D a   momentum before = momentum after
            0.3 kg × 2 m/s = 0.15 kg × velocity
            0.6 kg m/s = 0.15 kg × velocity
            velocity = 4 m/s to the right.
       b   momentum is conserved / it is a closed system
       c   either trolley **X** is moving faster, or trolley **Y** is moving slower; the momentum after the collision is not zero, but in the direction of trolley **X**

P10.5

A   conservation, forces, total momentum
        explosion, different directions, zero
B   when the man tries to leap, he exerts a force backwards on his boat, causing the boat to gain momentum in the reverse direction; his boat moves backwards, the gap between the boats increases, and the man cannot leap the full distance
C   momentum before collision
            = (75 × 6.0) + (80 × 2.0)
            = 610
        speed after collision $= \frac{610}{75 + 80} = 3.9\,\text{m/s}$
D   as the gas escapes from a nozzle it gains momentum in the direction in which the nozzle points; momentum of the astronaut–gas system must be conserved, so the astronaut must gain an equal momentum in the opposite direction

P10.6

A   forces, duration / time, greater / larger / higher
        momentum, momentum, mΔv
        equal, opposite, opposite
B a   change in velocity = –15 m/s,
            $\text{deceleration} = \frac{15}{0.25} = 60\,\text{m/s}^2$
       b   average F = ma = 550 × 60 = 3300 N
            (3.3 kN)
       c   3300 N (3.3 kN)
C a   the crumple zones crumple during impact, making the impact happen over a longer period of time; this reduces the deceleration and therefore the force on each car during the collision
       b   5.0 m/s to the right
       c   the cars have the same masses and momentum as in **B** and so after the same test collision they have the same velocity

P10.7

A increase / lengthen, duration / time
windscreen, time, force, large, pressure
air bags, reduce

B

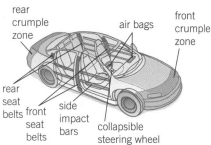

rear crumple zone
air bags
front crumple zone
rear seat belts
front seat belts
side impact bars
collapsible steering wheel

C a during the thinking distance the car continues at its original speed because no braking force has been applied, so the distance travelled is proportional to the speed (distance = speed × time)

  b during the braking distance the car is decelerating; assuming the braking force is constant, the deceleration is constant ($F = ma$) and we can use the relationship $s = \dfrac{-u^2}{2a}$ to show that $s \propto u^2$ where s is the distance travelled, a is the deceleration, and u is the initial speed

P10.8

A elastic
difference
directly proportional, proportionality, linear
proportionality, non-linear, proportional

B a apply a force to the material and release it; an elastic material goes back to its original shape when you remove the force, but a plastic material does not

  b force and extension

C a extension = 4.5 cm – 3 cm
= 1.5 cm = 0.015 m
force = 40 N/m × 0.015 m
= 0.6 N

  b if the force trebles, the extension trebles
extension = 3 × 0.015 m = 0.045 m
so length = 0.03 m + 0.045 m = 0.075 m
= 7.5 cm

D a the first section of the graph is a straight line, so extension is proportional to force

  b sample would not return to its original length / it would be permanently stretched

  c two appropriate measurements used (e.g. 2 N / 2 cm, 4 N / 4 cm)
$$\text{spring constant} = \frac{\text{force}}{\text{extension}}$$
$$= \frac{4\,\text{N}}{0.04\,\text{m}}$$
$$= 100\,\text{N/m}$$

P10 Practice questions

01 speed affects the thinking distance [1] because you will travel further during your reaction time if your speed is higher; [1] speed affects the braking distance [1] because if you are travelling faster, the distance needed to stop whilst your brakes work will be longer; [1] stopping distance = thinking distance + braking distance [1] so your overall stopping distance will be larger [1]

02.1 0.0226 N, [1] 670 (m/s²), [1] 300 kg [1]

02.2 the mass in the column is the inertial mass because each mass = force/acceleration. [1]

03.1 3 m/s [1]

03.2 it travels at a steady speed / terminal velocity [1] because the forces are balanced; [1] the air resistance is equal to the weight [1]

04.1 acceleration $a = \dfrac{-u^2}{2s}$ [1]
$$= \frac{-(60\,\text{m/s})^2}{(2 \times 50\,\text{m})}\ [1]$$
$$= -36\,\text{m/s}^2\ [1]$$

04.2 $F = ma$ [1]
$F = 250\,000\,\text{kg} \times 36\,\text{m/s}^2$ [1]
$= 9\,000\,000\,\text{N}$ [1]

04.3 $\text{spring constant} = \dfrac{\text{force}}{\text{extension}}$ [1]
$$= \frac{9\,000\,000\,\text{N}}{10\,\text{m}}$$
$$= 900\,000\,\text{N/m}\ [1]$$

04.4 momentum = mv [1]
$= 250\,000\,\text{kg} \times 60\,\text{m/s}$
$= 15\,000\,000\,\text{kg m/s}$ [1]

05.1 $v^2 = u^2 + 2as$ [1]
$v^2 = 0 + 2 \times 9.8 \times 1.00 = 19.6$ [1]
$v = 4.4(3)\,\text{m/s}$ [1]

05.2 momentum = mv
$= 0.050 \times 4.43$
$= 0.22$ [1] kg m/s [1]

05.3 $F = m\dfrac{(v - u)}{t}$ [1]
$$= 0.050 \times \frac{4.43}{0.40}\ [1]$$
$$= 0.55\,\text{N}\ [1]$$

05.4 the force experienced by the egg was much smaller in the second impact [1] because the impact lasted a much longer time [1]

P11.1

A force, area
pascals / Pa, force (N), area (m²), $\dfrac{F}{A}$

B technique to weigh them and then measure the total area of their feet (e.g. drawing around paws and determining area); observe how many feet are on the ground at once when walking to find the area

C a area of one blade = 9.00×10^{-4} m²; for two skates, area = 18.00×10^{-4} m²
$$\text{pressure} = \frac{\text{weight}}{\text{area}}$$
$$= \frac{80 \times 9.8}{18.00 \times 10^{-4}} = 436\,\text{kPa}$$
$$= 440\,\text{kPa to 2 s.f.}$$

  b the Zamboni wheels have a much larger area in contact with the ice and so the pressure is much lower despite the Zamboni being much heavier than the skater

D a weight of rider = 55 × 9.8 = 539 N
area in contact with ground = 30 cm²
= 0.003 m²
$$\text{pressure} = \frac{F}{A} = \frac{539}{0.003}$$
$$= 1.8 \times 10^5\,\text{Pa or 180 kPa}$$

  b the weight of the bicycle and rider stays the same, so as the pressure decreases the area of tyre in contact with the road will increase (giving a 'flat tyre')

P11.2

A depth, weight
density of liquid (kg/m³), gravitational field strength (N/kg) (in either order), h

B a the holes are all at the same height; the pressure at this depth is the same all around the bottle

  b $p = h\rho$
$= 0.15 \times 1000 \times 9.8$
$= 1470\,\text{Pa} = 1500\,\text{Pa}$ (1.5 kPa) to 2 s.f.

C a 250 kN

  b 20 kN

  c there is a resultant force of 230 kN acting on the window which would push the window into the submarine if it did not have a wedge shape

P11.3

A molecules, surfaces, force
decreases, decreases, fewer
100 km

B a pressure at 4800 m is 55 kPa (accept range 54–58) so the change in pressure is 45 kPa (accept range 42–46)

  b $p = h\rho g$
$$\text{average}\ \rho = \frac{\Delta p}{\Delta h g}$$
$$= \frac{45 \times 10^3}{4800 \times 9.8}$$
$$= 0.96\,\text{kg/m}^3$$

C a

(graph: atmospheric pressure in kPa (y-axis 0–10 000) vs height above surface in km (x-axis 0–50), showing a decreasing curve)

  b the pressure shows the same pattern, decreasing with height (pressure is inversely proportional to height), but the pressure on Venus is nearly 100 times that on Earth

c $p = h\rho g$

average $\rho = \dfrac{\Delta p}{\Delta h g}$

$= \dfrac{9210 \times 10^3 - 6665 \times 10^3}{5000 \times 8.9}$

$= 57\ \text{kg/m}^3$

P11.4

A fluid / liquid, upthrust, pressure
weight, greater / bigger

B a 0.1 N

b 2.0; 2.7; 3.2

c the upthrust would be smaller in each case; the pressure difference between the top and bottom surfaces of the rock would be smaller because pressure is proportional to the density of the liquid; so the resultant upward force would be smaller

C a $150 \times 10^3 \times 9.8 = 1.47 \times 10^6\ \text{N}$ or 1470 kN

b

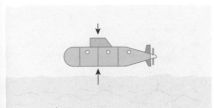

c the pressure difference means that the bottom surface of the submarine has a greater force acting on it from the pressure of the water than the top surface has; this difference in the size of the forces gives a resultant force upwards, or upthrust on the submarine; if this upthrust is equal to the weight of the submarine it will remain at the same depth

P11 Practice questions

1.1 total area of contact = $4 \times 0.05 = 0.2\ \text{m}^2$ [1]
$p = \dfrac{F}{A} = \dfrac{40\,500}{0.2} = 203$ [1] kPa [1]

1.2 area = $2.0\ \text{mm}^2 = 2.0 \times 10^{-6}\ \text{m}^2$ [1]
$F = \dfrac{p}{A} = 203\,000 \times 2.0 \times 10^{-6} = 0.4\ \text{N}$ [1]

2.1 the pressure is the same at both points [1]

2.2 $p = h\rho g$ [1] = $0.120 \times 1000 \times 9.8 = 1176$
= 1180 [1] Pa [1] (or 1.18 [1] kPa [1]) to 3 s.f.

2.3 $\rho = \dfrac{p}{hg}$ [1] = $\dfrac{1176}{0.142 \times 9.8} = 845$ [1] kg/m³ [1]

2.4 the level of the top of the oil column would rise up the tube [1] and the level of the top of the water column would fall until they reach a new equilibrium [1]

.1 pressure due to water
$p = h\rho g$
= $12.0 \times 1030 \times 9.8$ [1]
= 121 128 Pa
= 121 000 Pa or 121 kPa [1] to 3 s.f.
add atmospheric pressure of 100 kPa to give total pressure = 221 kPa [1]

2 $F = p \times A$ [1] = $221 \times 10^3 \times 2.4$
= 530×10^3 N or 530 kN [1]

03.3 force on internal side of glass = $100\,000 \times 2.4$
= 240 kN [1]
resultant force = 530 − 240 = 290 kN [1]

03.4 upthrust = weight = $15\,000 \times 9.8 = 147$ kN [1]

03.5 the pressure on the bottom of the submarine is larger than the pressure acting on the top; [1] the pressure difference means that there is a larger force acting on the bottom surface than the top surface; [1] the difference in these forces causes an upthrust or buoyancy force [1] which matches the weight of the submarine [1]

P12.1

A information
transverse, ripples, electromagnetic
longitudinal, sound
medium

B a move her hand at 90° to the direction of the rope

b a longitudinal wave vibrates in the same direction as the wave travels; it is not possible to make a rope vibrate in this way

c information or energy

C a wave B; the ground is moving at 90° to the direction of the wave

b a compression is where the material is compressed / particles are closer together; a rarefaction is where the material is stretched / particles are further apart

c they need a medium to travel through

P12.2

A maximum, peak, trough
same, peak, peak, (or trough/trough)

(s), $\dfrac{1}{\text{frequency (Hz)}}$

(m/s), frequency (Hz) × wavelength (m)

B period = $\dfrac{1}{200\ \text{Hz}}$
= 0.005 s

C a speed = $660\ \text{Hz} \times 0.5\ \text{m}$
= 330 m/s

b 0.25 m

c frequency = $\dfrac{\text{speed}}{\text{wavelength}}$
= $\dfrac{4000\ \text{m/s}}{70\ \text{m}}$
= 57 Hz

D a *The distance from one peak to the next peak is the wavelength. Frequency is the number of waves per second. The unit of frequency is seconds. The unit of wavelength is metres. The distance from a peak to a trough is the amplitude.*

b The unit of frequency is Hertz (Hz). The maximum displacement / distance of a peak or a trough from its rest / undisturbed position is the amplitude.

P12.3

A same, speed
refracted, zero
refraction
transmitted, absorbed

B a reflection: dashed lines drawn at equal angles, as in Figure 1 on page 140 of the Student Book; refraction: dashed lines parallel to the new direction, but further apart

b arrow top left continued until it hits the mirror, then a line drawn at equal angles; line at 90° to the mirror where the arrow hits the mirror; angle of incidence labelled from the normal to the incident ray; angle of reflection labelled from the normal to the angle of reflection

c the wavelength increases because the speed is increasing and the frequency is the same

d both waves change speed, both waves change wavelength; the wavelength of the waves in diagram **Y** increases because the speed increases; they are refracted because the direction changes; in diagram **Z**, the wavelength decreases because the speed decreases, but the direction does not change so they are not refracted

C as light travels through water, it can be transmitted or absorbed; the amount that is absorbed depends on the depth of water; some light is absorbed but some is transmitted through a smaller depth of water, as from the bottom of a swimming pool, so you can see it; most / all light is absorbed by very deep water, so does not reach the bottom of a deep ocean

P12.4

A reflects
time, distance
m/s, $\dfrac{\text{distance (m)}}{\text{time (s)}}$

B a a reflection of sound

b measure a long distance from a large building using a measuring tape or a metre rule; stand that distance away; make a short loud sound using the blocks and start a stopwatch; stop the stopwatch when you hear the echo of the sound; multiply the distance by 2 to use in the equation; use the equation
speed = $\dfrac{\text{distance}}{\text{time}}$ to calculate the speed

c total distance travelled by the sound
= 2 × distance to wall = 2×150 m
= 300 m
speed = $\dfrac{300\ \text{m}}{0.90\ \text{s}}$
= 333.3 m/s = 330 m/s to 2 s.f.

d reasonable estimates, e.g. 5 cm, 0.2 s

e the biggest difference in the speed would be if the distance was 145 cm, or 1.45 m, and the time was 0.7 s, giving a
speed of $145\ \text{m} \times \dfrac{2}{0.7\ \text{s}} = 414\ \text{m/s}$

P12.5

A music, repeating, noise
echo sounding, reflects
ears, ear drum, brain
speed, wavelength, frequency, limited range

B **a** 0.66
b 500
c 1700

C **a** time taken for pulse to reach sea floor = 0.15 s; distance = 1500 × 0.15 = 225 m
b sound wave pulse would increase in speed in the denser water and so return to the boat in a slightly shorter time than expected; so the depth reading would be too small (in practice, only by a few cm for this depth of seawater)

D below 20 Hz no sound would be heard because our ears do not respond to these very low frequencies; above 20 Hz a sound should be heard (by someone with normal hearing) but at low volume initially because our ears are not very sensitive to this low frequency; as the frequency increases to 3000 Hz, the pitch and perceived volume both increase as our ears are most responsive at this frequency; above 3000 Hz the pitch continues to increase but the volume seems to decrease because our ears become less responsive until no sound at all is heard at around 20 kHz and above

P12.6

A 20 kHz / 20 000 Hz, ears
organs / tissues, transducer, partially reflected, transmitted / non-reflected, reflected
cracks

B

	X-ray	Ultrasound
Example procedure	imaging a bone fracture	prenatal scan
Advantages	high contrast between bone and soft tissue	non-ionising so does not damage living cells
	high resolution (can show fine detail)	can distinguish between different types of soft tissue
Disadvantages	ionising so can damage living cells	lower resolution

C ultrasound waves are longitudinal waves, like other sound waves; we cannot hear ultrasound because it has too high a frequency for our ears to detect; X-rays are transverse high-frequency waves that are part of the electromagnetic spectrum; we cannot see either ultrasound waves or X-rays; X-rays can cause harmful ionisation in our cells but ultrasound cannot

D **a** there is an extra signal, showing the detection of a partially reflected pulse, which must be produced by reflection from a crack or other sudden change in density

b time between reflection from outer surface and inner surface of pipe = 5.0 μs
time for pulse to to travel from outer to inner surface of pipe = 2.5 μs
depth = speed × time = 4600 × 2.5 × 10⁻⁶
= 0.012 m or 12 mm

P12.7

A seismic waves, longitudinal, transverse
seismometer, internal structure

B **a** density of the mantle changes / increases with depth, causing a change in speed of the waves and hence refraction
b outer core is liquid; S-waves are transverse; transverse waves cannot pass through liquids
c S-waves cannot travel through the outer core and so cannot reach the shadow zone; P-waves are refracted as they enter the outer core and again when they leave it, resulting in no P-waves reaching the shadow zone

C a large disturbance needed such as an impact or an explosion; this would produce waves travelling through the crust, mantle, and core; seismometers could detect waves at different points on Mars and the pattern could be analysed to determine the thicknesses of the layers and whether or not there is a liquid outer core

P12 Practice questions

01.1 mechanical waves need a medium to travel through, but electromagnetic waves do not [1]

01.2 electromagnetic waves have a very high speed / 300 million m/s, but mechanical waves travel much more slowly [1]

02.1 speed = frequency × wavelength [1]
= 1000 Hz × 1.5 m [1]
= 1500 m/s [1]

02.2 period = $\dfrac{1}{\text{frequency}}$ [1]
= $\dfrac{1}{1000}$ Hz [1]
= 0.001 s [1

02.3 distance pulse travels (there and back) = 1500 × 0.12 = 180 m [1]
so depth of fish = 90 m [1]

03.1 diagram showing incoming wave crests and outgoing wave crests at 90° (correct by eye); [1] a barrier in an appropriate position (at 45° to the direction of incoming and outgoing wave direction) [1]

03.2 reflection [1]

03.3 transmission [1] and absorption [1]

04.1 they started the timer when they saw the sound being made [1] and stopped the timer when they heard it [1]

04.2 total distance travelled by the sound = 2 × distance to wall = 2 × 200 m
= 400 m [1]
speed = $\dfrac{400 \text{ m}}{1.3 \text{ s}}$ [1]
= 307.7 m/s [1] = 310 m/s [1]

04.3 repeat the experiment / take more measurements of time and calculate the mean time [1]

05 **six** from: the shock wave travels through the layers of rock; [1] partial reflection at layer boundaries; [1] reflections detected by seismograph; [1] timing information collected; [1] wave travels at different speeds in different types of rock; [1] thickness of layers can be determined from timing information and speed; [1] wave travels through layers twice (due to reflection) so distances must be halved to find thickness [1]

P13.1

A microwave, infrared, visible light, ultraviolet, X-rays
longest, shortest, lowest, highest
visible light, 350, 650
source, detector
wave speed (m/s) = frequency (Hz) × wavelength (m)

B **a** radio waves
b radio / microwaves / infrared / visible
c gamma
d radio / microwaves / infrared
e any apart from infrared
f radio waves

C wavelength = 0.03 m
speed = 10 000 000 000 Hz × 0.03 m
= 300 000 000 m/s

D biggest wavelength = 650 nm
= 650 × 10⁻⁹ m
so smallest frequency
$f = \dfrac{v}{\lambda}$
= $\dfrac{300\,000\,000 \text{ m/s}}{650 \times 10^{-9} \text{ m}}$ = 4.6 × 10¹⁴ Hz
smallest wavelength = 350 nm
= 350 × 10⁻⁹ m
so biggest frequency
$f = \dfrac{v}{\lambda}$
= $\dfrac{300\,000\,000 \text{ m/s}}{350 \times 10^{-9} \text{ m}}$ = 8.6 × 10¹⁴ Hz

P13.2

A waves
information, optical
radio, microwaves, microwaves, radio waves
radio, microwaves, infrared

B infrared cameras detect infrared radiation given out by objects, but remote controls emit it
remote controls use infrared radiation to transmit information, but infrared cameras use the infrared radiation they detect to produce an image, and so provide information

C **a** skin detects the heat from infrared waves and eyes detect light waves
b point a remote control at a wall and see you can still change channel

c you can detect microwaves using your mobile phone, and radio waves using a television or radio whilst inside your house

a $\dfrac{2.45\text{ GHz}}{0.1\text{ GHz}} = 24.5$ (no unit)

b the energy of microwaves used in the microwave oven is much higher than the energy of microwaves used in the mobile phone (24.5 times higher); the frequency of microwaves for mobile phones needs to be so much lower, otherwise it could pose a risk to human health; the frequency of microwaves for microwave ovens needs to be high, otherwise it would not cook food

13.3

distance, spread, information, information, amplitude

microwaves

evidence

visible, infrared

a **X, Z, W, Y**

b **i** unlike radio waves, microwaves do not spread out, and are not absorbed by the atmosphere.

    ii local radio stations use shorter wavelength radio waves because the range over which they need to be transmitted is not as far as those needed for national radio stations

a infrared radiation is used to send signals down optical fibres

b microwaves have a heating effect, but the infrared radiation is contained inside the optical fibres

a **Y, X, Z**

b a radio transmitter uses the audio signal to modulate the carrier wave, then transmits the modulated wave; a radio receiver receives the radio signal, separates the audio signal from the carrier wave, and emits the audio signal

13.4

shorter, skin

hospitals / medicine

bacteria, sterilise, cancer

ionising

damage

a ultraviolet is less penetrating than X-rays or gamma waves, so does not penetrate further than the skin; it cannot damage cells inside the body to cause cancer

b an X-ray or a gamma ray passes through human tissue; as it passes through, the X-ray or gamma ray knocks an electron out of an atom; this process is called ionisation; ionisation can kill cells or damage the DNA of a cell; damaged DNA can cause cancer

c the shorter the wavelength, the higher the risk of damage to DNA

d kill harmful bacteria on food / sterilise surgical equipment / kill cancer cells

C the Earth is protected by the ozone layer, which absorbs ultraviolet radiation, just as sunscreen does

D X-rays and gamma rays are different because they have different wavelengths / frequencies; X-rays are produced by fast-moving electrons, but gamma rays are produced in nuclear decay; X-rays and gamma rays are similar because they are both forms of ionising radiation, and they can both cause cancer inside the body

P13.5

A cancer

ionising, low, high

absorb

B **a** produce images of internal body parts

    b kill skin cancer cells

    c kill cancer cells inside the body

C **a** to stop exposure to visible light

    b lines that end on the bone, but go through the gap in the middle; explanation: the bone absorbs the X-rays, so they do not reach the film, and it is not exposed; the skin / muscle does not absorb X-rays (as much) so they do reach the film; the image on the film shows areas that X-rays have reached

    c lead: it is very dense and absorbs X-rays

D **a** $\dfrac{2\text{ mSv}}{0.1\text{ mSv}} = 20$

    b a doctor might be more likely to ask for a chest X-ray because it gives a patient 5% of their annual dose, but less likely to order a whole-body scan because it give a patient 5 times their annual dose; if a person's dose is higher, the risk of cancer is higher, so the condition being treated would need to be serious so that the benefits of the scan outweigh the risk

P13 Practice questions

01.1 radio, microwave, infrared, visible, ultraviolet, X-rays, gamma

[radio before microwave, microwave before infrared, infrared before visible, visible before ultraviolet, ultraviolet before X-rays, X-rays before gamma – 1 mark each]

01.2 they are in order of increasing frequency [1]

01.3 visible light [1]

02.1 for example:

1. microwave oven, [1] microwaves [1]
2. remote control, [1] infrared [1]

02.2 for example:

1. TV aerial, [1] radio waves [1]
2. radio, [1] radio waves [1]

03.1 a high frequency electromagnetic wave used to carry information [1]

03.2 they carry more information / they do not spread out as much [1]

03.3 microwaves are used in a microwave oven to heat food, but microwaves are

used in mobile phones to send / receive information [1]

the mobile phone radiation does not produce a heating effect that can cook food [1]

so it must have a smaller frequency / energy, and a bigger wavelength [1]

03.4 doing experiments on people involves ethical issues; [1] it is difficult to measure the heating effect / damage of microwave radiation on the brain [1]

04.1 radiation that removes electrons from atoms / molecules when it passes through matter [1]

04.2 in the parts that are white, the X-rays are absorbed by bone [1] so do not reach the CCD / photographic film, so no radiation = white; [1] the X-rays reach the CCD / photographic film through skin / muscle so radiation = black [1]

04.3 **two** from: shielding; [1] reducing time spent near source; [1] increasing distance between source and person [1]

explanation: reduces damage to DNA from ionisation so reduces the risk of cancer [1]

05 wavelength $= \dfrac{\text{speed}}{\text{frequency}}$ [1]

$= \dfrac{300\,000\,000\text{ m/s}}{100\,000\,000\text{ Hz}}$ [1]

$= 3\text{ m}$ [1]

06.1 X-rays are not absorbed (noticeably) by the kidneys [1]

06.2 when you have an X-ray, the source is outside the body, not inside; [1] so during an X-ray, the patient can be shielded with lead, but when a gamma camera is used, they cannot [1]

P14.1

A incidence, reflection, normal, perpendicular / at 90°

virtual, same distance

specular reflection, diffuse reflection

B

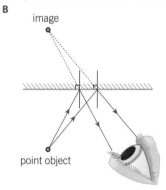

C **a** protractor

    b 1°

    c 30°–55°

    d random error

    e repeat the measurements for each angle of incidence several times and calculate the mean values for the angle of reflection

D

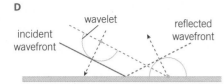

incident wavefront — wavelet — reflected wavefront

a wavefront can be considered to consist of many wavelets; when each wavelet on a wavefront reaches a reflective surface it creates a wavelet moving away from the barrier; when all of the reflected wavelets combine they produce a reflected wavefront that moves off at the same angle (on the other side of the normal) as the original wavefront

P14.2

A   refracted, speed
decreases, towards, perpendicular, direction

B

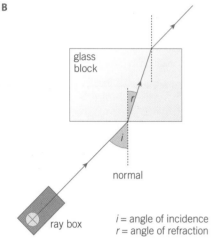

glass block

normal

ray box   *i* = angle of incidence
r = angle of refraction

set up a ray box and the block on a large sheet of paper; shine a ray of light from the ray box into the block at measured angles of incidence; complete the ray paths and measure the corresponding angles of refraction with a protractor; plot a graph of angle of incidence against angle of refraction to see if there is any pattern

C

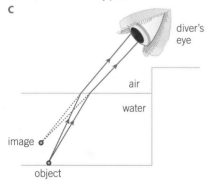

diver's eye

air

water

image

object

rays from the bottom of the pool refract away from the normal at the water surface and into the diver's eye; this creates a virtual image of the object higher up in the pool (dotted line) which makes it look as if the pool is shallower

D   white light is composed of a range of wavelengths; each wavelength of light travels at a different speed in the glass and so refracts by different amounts at the rear boundary; we see the different wavelengths

of light as different colours, so this experiment shows the white light splitting (dispersing) into its constituent colours / a spectrum

P14.3

A   transparent, scattering, refraction, opaque

B   **a**

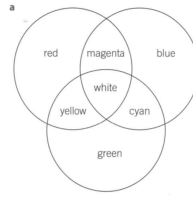

red   magenta   blue
white
yellow   cyan
green

(allow any orientation and order of the red, green, and blue circles; allow 'turquoise' for cyan and 'pink' or 'purple' for magenta)

   b   everywhere the original red light reaches would look red, because the red paper will reflect red light; all of the other areas would look black because the red card will only reflect red light and absorb other colours

C   **a**   lasers emit a single frequency / wavelength (or a very narrow band of frequencies / wavelengths), while filament lamps emit a broad band of frequencies (white or yellowish white)

   b   the green lenses act as green filters; the red laser light would not pass through and damage the eye

D   Sun's surface temperature is close to 6000 K and so it emits radiation very similar to the 6000 K profile, i.e. most visible wavelengths of light fairly evenly, and so appears whiteish (in space); Betelgeuse is cooler and emits much more red light than any other colour so appears red; Rigel emits much more blue and violet light than red and so appears bluish

P14.4

A   refracting, convex, principal focus, concave, principal focus
closer / nearer, larger / bigger
image size
object size

B   **a**   575
   b   27.9 m
   c   it is a ratio (of two lengths)

C

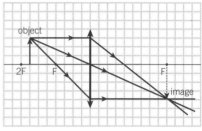

a   convex   **b**   concave

focal length   focal length

D   white light consists of a spectrum of colours which travel at different speed through the lens and so refract differently; this causes the light of different colours to spread when they enter and leave the lens; the effect is greatest when the angles of incidence are larger which happens with highly curved lenses

P14.5

A   convex, real, clear / focused, further
virtual

B   **a**

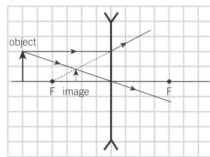

object   2F   F   F   image

   b   inverted / upside down, magnified / larger than the object, real

C   **a**

object   F   image   F

   b   upright / same way up as object, diminished / smaller than object, virtual

D   **a**   convex / converging
   b   shine parallel rays from a ray box through the lens and measure the point at which the rays cross to find the focal length; then adjust the curvature of the lens by stretching the fabric it rests on to stretch the lens, or by using the ruler to trim the lens

P14 Practice questions

01.1   rectangular glass block, ray box (and power supply), sheet of white paper, protractor, pencil, ruler [1 for simple list; 1 for comprehensive list including protractor]

01.2

emergent ray

angle of refraction
refracted ray
normal
angle of incidence
glass block
incident ray
ray b

diagram showing rays entering and leaving glass block [1] with angles identified [1]

01.3 place block on paper and draw around it; draw normal at 90° to one face; using protractor draw in angles of incidence of 20°, 30°, 40°, 50°, 60°; shine ray of light from ray box along each line and draw in emergent ray each time; remove block and join incident and emergent rays; measure angle of refraction [1 for simple outline method; 2 for more detailed method containing nearly all required steps; 3 for full method with all required steps and details of measurements to be taken]

02.1 distance between ray box and light meter; [1] brightness of lamp / power to ray box [1]

02.2 white light consists of a spectrum of colours; [1] the red filter absorbs all of the colours of light except red [1]

02.3 the meter is detecting a greater light intensity so more of the light must be passing through [1]

02.4 the light meter is equally responsive to all colours / wavelengths of light [1]

03.1

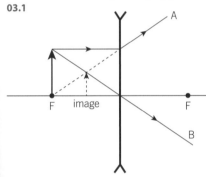

ray A, [1] ray B, [1] image [1]

03.2 upright, [1] diminished / smaller than the object, [1] virtual [1]

04.1 object distance [1]

04.2 magnification [1]

04.3 image size ÷ object size [1]

04.4

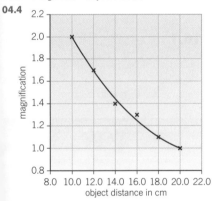

suitable (even) scales; [1] points plotted accurately; [1] line of best fit [1]

04.5 magnification is inversely proportional to object distance [1] (accept any inverse relationship)

P15.1

repel, attract
north, south
induced
steel
iron

B put the permanent magnet near one end of the bar; turn the bar through 180°; if the bar is only attracted to the magnet, then it is made of a magnetic material; if one end of the bar repels the magnet then it is a magnet itself

C a new paperclips are not magnetic / are not induced magnets

b steel; when you put a steel paper clip in a magnetic field it becomes an induced magnet, and will attract other magnetic materials; steel is a hard magnetic material, and will stay magnetic when the magnetic field that made it magnetic is removed

D a

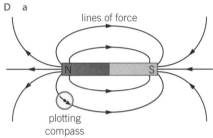

lines of force

plotting compass

b when the compass is near the magnet it will line up with the magnetic field of the magnet; as you move the compass away it will eventually line up with the magnetic field of the Earth

P15.2

A circles
parallel
increasing, reverse
parallel

B a concentric circles getting further apart; arrows to show field is clockwise

b the arrows would go in a anticlockwise direction

C a a solenoid is a coil of wire, and an electromagnet is produced when a current flows in the coil of wire

b the magnetic field inside an electromagnet is strong and uniform; the field lines are parallel inside; the field outside is looped like the field of a bar magnet, with the complete loops passing inside as well

D a the number of coils, the type of core

b a graph with a positive gradient (straight line)
y-axis labelled 'mass of iron filings'; x-axis labelled 'current'

c as you increase the current the strength of the electromagnet increases, so the mass of iron filings increases.

d advantage: the strength can be measured more accurately by finding mass
disadvantage: the paperclips are easier to remove from the electromagnet in order to count them

---

P15.3

A current, magnetic field
breaker, current, large / big / high), relay

B a

The button is pressed	→	A current flows in the coil
The armature is attracted to the electromagnet	←	The coil and its core act as an electromagnet
The hammer strikes the bell	→	The circuit is broken
The circuit is reconnected	←	The armature is pulled back by the springy metal strip

b the iron core becomes magnetic when there is a current and quickly loses its magnetism when there is no current

C a a systematic error, because all measured values will be lower than they should be by the weight of the bar

b there is a fairly large variation in the results for each test, so precision is low

c the greater the number of loops of wire, the greater the strength of the electromagnet; and the greater the current, the stronger the electromagnet

P15.4

A increase, reverse
coil
flux density
N, magnetic field strength (T) × current (A) × length (m)

B a the wire needs to be at right angles to the magnetic field

b $F = BIl$
$= 0.4\,T \times 2.0\,A \times 0.2\,m$
$= 0.16\,N$

c $I = \dfrac{F}{B \times l}$

$= \dfrac{0.05\,N}{0.4\,T \times 0.2\,m}$

$= 0.625\,A\ (0.63\,A)$

C a arrow starting on dot and pointing vertically up

b a coil of current-carrying wire in a magnetic field that can spin

c spin in the opposite direction; spin more slowly; spin faster

P15.5

A magnet, potential difference, generator, current, opposes

B a anticlockwise
b north pole
c attract
d anticlockwise
e north pole
f repel
g clockwise
h south pole
i attract

C **a** connect the equipment as shown in the diagram; move the wire through the magnetic field and note the current reading on the ammeter; the current pulse shows that a p.d. was produced by the wire moving through the magnetic field

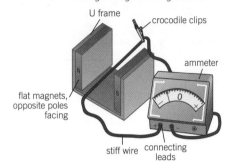

b make these changes: increase the speed of movement, reverse the direction of movement, reverse the magnetic field; and note the change in induced current

D equipment: bar magnet, wooden pole / stick / similar (to help push magnet in and out), solenoid, ruler, stopclock, ammeter, leads
method: connect the coil to the ammeter, attach the magnet to the end of the stick, move the magnet into the coil at a steady speed, use the ruler and stopclock to measure speed in cm/s, record the peak current during the movement; repeat at gradually increasing speeds

P15.6

A alternating current, magnetic field, potential difference / induced p.d. / induced voltage
dynamo, split-ring, direction
microphone, sound, vibrate, electrical signal / induced p.d. / induced voltage / induced current, frequency
alternating current / electrical signal, frequency

B **a**

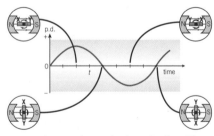

(accept the two horizontal coil positions swapped and the two vertical coil positions swapped)

b

(field lines not essential; accept X and Y swapped to match answer to part **a**)

C **a, b**

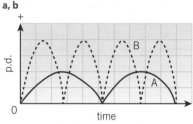

c every second p.d. peak would be in the negative direction

P15.7

A potential difference, primary, secondary, iron core, magnetic field, induce

B **a** the a.c. in the primary coil causes an alternating magnetic field in the iron core; the alternating magnetic field induces an alternating p.d. in the secondary coil; if the number of turns on the secondary coil is greater than the number of turns on the primary then the output/secondary p.d. will be greater than the input/primary p.d., and vice versa

b the process needs a changing magnetic field; a d.c. supply would provide a constant magnetic field

C **a** **i** input voltage; **ii** output voltage; **iii** turns of wire on primary, turns of wire on secondary; **iv** output voltage is directly proportional to input voltage; **v** turns of wire on secondary; **vi** output voltage; **vii** turns of wire on primary, input voltage; **viii** output voltage is directly proportional to number of turns on secondary

b 0.01 V

c the transformer could act as a step-up transformer; if the input voltage were not limited, the transformer could increase the voltage to a dangerous level

P15.8

A step-up, more, step-down, fewer
p.d. across secondary coil, n_p

B **a** 18.4

b 30

c 300

d 850

C **a** for a given power output, high p.d. means low current ($P = IV$); current has a heating effect, which depends on the square of the current ($P = I^2R$); so reducing the current gives a large reduction in heating effect / energy losses / power wastage

b high voltages are dangerous and could cause electrocution if used in homes

D **a** transformer 1: 99.8%; transformer 2: 89.8%

b transformer 2 is faulty; the efficiency of a transformer should be very near 100%

P15 Practice questions

01.1 arrow on the long left side of the coil pointing up coil (towards commutator); [1] arrow on the long right side of the coil pointing down coil (away from commutator) [1]

01.2 the coil would spin the opposite way [1]

01.3 magnetic flux density

$$= \frac{\text{force}}{\text{length} \times \text{current}} \text{ [1 – or implie}$$

$$= \frac{0.005 \text{ N}}{0.05 \text{ m} \times 1.2 \text{ A}}$$

$$= 0.08 \text{ [1] T [1]}$$

02.1 a step-down transformer: the output voltages are smaller than the corresponding input voltages [1]

02.2 input and output values for p.d. taken fro graph; [1] use of equation $\frac{V_p}{V_s} = \frac{n_p}{n_s}$ [1] to give $3.0 = \frac{50}{n_s}$ [1] and $n_s = 22$ [1]

02.3 output p.d. read from graph or calculated as 2.0 V [1]
primary p.d. × primary current = seconda p.d. × secondary current [1]
$6.0 \times 0.5 = 2.0 \times$ lamp current [1]
lamp current = 1.5 A [1]

02.4 the transformer is 100% efficient [1]

03.1 alternating potential difference; the generator is an alternator because it has slip rings and brushes (and not a split-rin commutator) [1]

03.2 (see diagram below, curve A) sinusoidal wave; [1] period 0.4 s; [1] equal positive a negative amplitude [1]

03.3 (see diagram below, curve B) period 0.8 s; lower peak voltage than A [1]

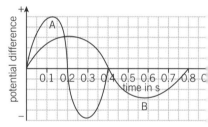

P16.1

A gas, gravitational, protostar, hydrogen, fuse together
main sequence, gravity, radiation

B

Size rank	Object	Key features
2	gas giant	the four outer planets; low density; orbit the Sun
5	asteroid	a small (non-spherical) rock object; one of billions; man found in the asteroid belt between Mars and Jupiter
1	Sun	a (main sequence) star; produces radiation due to nuclear fusion; at the centr of the Solar system
3	terrestrial (rocky) planet	the four inner planets; dense; orbit the Sun
4	moon	a spherical rocky object tha orbits a planet

C the resultant of the gravitational attraction of the particles which make up the Sun is directed inwards; it is balanced by an outward force caused by radiation pressure, due to gamma radiation emitted outwards from the core of the Sun in nuclear fusion reactions

D **a** as the star is compressed by gravitational forces it gets denser; the particles speed up and collide more; this raises the internal temperature of the star

b protostars are dim/faint; they only emit infrared radiation due to their temperature; this cannot penetrate our atmosphere

P16.2

A hydrogen, core, red giant, fused
white dwarf, black dwarf
supergiant, supernova
neutron star, black hole, light

B *see image at bottom of column*

C gold is a heavy element which was formed when lighter elements underwent nuclear fusion in supernova explosions, and were thrown outwards in a cloud of debris (a nebula); eventually some of this debris formed our Solar System

D **a** it does not have enough mass to result in a supernova explosion

b a huge increase in Antares' brightness (it would become about as bright as a full moon) for a period of several days or weeks, which would be observed on Earth nearly 5 centuries later

P16.3

A centripetal force, centre, perpendicular / at right angles, acceleration
slower, longer

B **a, b**

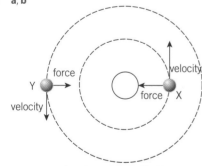

c each moon experiences a centripetal force produced by gravity; this accelerates the moon constantly towards the planet; since the acceleration is perpendicular to the moon's movement, it causes a change in direction but no change in speed; the moon is constantly pulled towards the planet, resulting in a circular path with the planet at the centre

C **a** distance signal travels = 72 000 km

$$t = \frac{d}{v} = \frac{72\,000}{300\,000} = 0.24\,\text{s}$$

b at closer distances the satellite would need to travel at a higher speed to orbit the Earth; it would complete each revolution in less than 24 hours so would not stay in the same place in the sky

c radius of orbit (*r*) = 36 000 km + 6400 km
= 42 400 km

distance travelled = circumference of orbit = 2π*r* = π × 84 800 = 266 400 km

$$\text{speed} = \frac{\text{distance}}{\text{time}} = \frac{266\,000\,\text{km}}{24\,\text{hours}}$$
$$= 11\,100\,\text{km/h}$$

P16.4

A away from, wavelength, redder, red-shift, faster
further away, greater, expanding

B

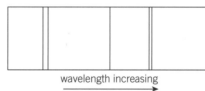

wavelength increasing →

a

red-shifted

b

blue-shifted

C **a** scientists were confident with their previous theory and required overwhelming evidence to replace it

b the previous theory could not explain the observations; more evidence about the motion of galaxies was gathered

D for example: drawing galaxies on the surface of a balloon and inflating it; similarity that all 'galaxies' on the balloon move away from all others; limitation that expansion is across a 2D surface while the universe expands in 3D

P16.5

A small, dense, hot (*first three answers in any order*), expanded
cosmic microwave background radiation, increased, expanded, short, electromagnetic spectrum

B current universe: cold, large volume, low density
very early universe: very high temperature, very dense, very low volume

C **a**

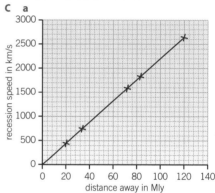

b gradient = 22 km/s/Mly

c 2200 km/s

D

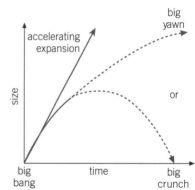

(allow any line of increasing gradient, i.e. curving upwards)

P16 Practice questions

01 a cloud of gas and dust (nebula) [1]
collapsed and heated up due to gravitational forces, producing a protostar / star; [1]
remaining materials were pulled into orbit around the star and pulled together by their own gravity to form planets [1]

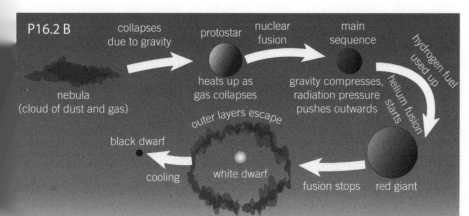

P16.2 B
nebula (cloud of dust and gas) — collapses due to gravity → protostar — heats up as gas collapses — nuclear fusion → main sequence — gravity compresses, radiation pressure pushes outwards — hydrogen fuel used up, helium fusion starts → red giant — fusion stops → white dwarf — cooling → black dwarf — outer layers escape

Answers

02 **six** from: (nebula containing) gas and dust collapses due to gravitational forces, [1] forming a protostar, which heats up until fusion starts; [1] hydrogen fuses to form helium; [1] helium fuses to form heavier elements; [1] it becomes a red supergiant; [1] fusion stops, star collapses and explodes as supernova; [1] remaining core forms a neutron star or black hole [1]

03.1

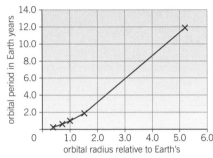

scatter graph with correctly labelled axes; [1] suitable scales; [1] accurately plotted points; [1] line of best fit [1]

03.2 as the orbital radius increases, so does the orbital period; [1] but the relationship is not linear / proportional [1]

03.3 5.2 (± 0.2) Earth years [1]

04.1 very dense; [1] very hot; [1] very small [1]

04.2 **four** from: it shows that distant galaxies are moving away from us; [1] assuming there is nothing special about our own galaxy, this means that all galaxies are moving away from one another; [1] it shows that the further away a galaxy is, the greater its red-shift; [1] meaning the faster it is travelling; [1] this relationship indicates that in the distant past were in the same place; [1] meaning that the universe was very much smaller [1]

05.1 blue-shifted means the spectral lines are at a shorter wavelength than those from an object not moving relative to the observer; [1] Andromeda is moving towards us [1]

05.2 spectral lines from region X show blue-sh compared to region Y, which means X is moving (relative to Y) towards us; [1] lines from region Z shows red-shift compared t Y, which means Z is moving (relative to Y) away from us; [1] these observations can be explained by the galaxy rotating [1]

Appendix 1: Physics equations

You should be able to remember and apply the following equations, using SI units, in your assessments.

Word equation	Symbol equation
weight = mass × gravitational field strength	$W = mg$
force applied to a spring = spring constant × extension	$F = ke$
acceleration = $\dfrac{\text{change in velocity}}{\text{time taken}}$	$a = \dfrac{\Delta v}{t}$
momentum = mass × velocity	$p = mv$
gravitational potential energy = mass × gravitational field strength × height	$E_p = mgh$
power = $\dfrac{\text{work done}}{\text{time}}$	$P = \dfrac{W}{t}$
efficiency = $\dfrac{\text{useful power output}}{\text{total power input}}$	
charge flow = current × time	$Q = It$
power = potential difference × current	$P = VI$
energy transferred = power × time	$E = Pt$
density = $\dfrac{\text{mass}}{\text{volume}}$	$\rho = \dfrac{m}{V}$
work done = force × distance (along the line of action of the force)	$W = Fs$
distance travelled = speed × time	$s = vt$
resultant force = mass × acceleration	$F = ma$
kinetic energy = 0.5 × mass × (speed)²	$E_k = \dfrac{1}{2}mv^2$
power = $\dfrac{\text{energy transferred}}{\text{time}}$	$P = \dfrac{E}{t}$
efficiency = $\dfrac{\text{useful output energy transfer}}{\text{total input energy transfer}}$	
wave speed = frequency × wavelength	$v = f\lambda$
potential difference = current × resistance	$V = IR$
power = current² × resistance	$P = I^2R$
energy transferred = charge flow × potential difference	$E = QV$
pressure = $\dfrac{\text{force normal to a surface}}{\text{area of that surface}}$	$p = \dfrac{F}{A}$
moment of a force = force × distance (normal to direction of force)	$M = Fd$

You should be able to select and apply the following equations from the Physics equation sheet.

Word equation	Symbol equation
(final velocity)² − (initial velocity)² = 2 × acceleration × distance	$v^2 - u^2 = 2\,a\,s$
elastic potential energy = 0.5 × spring constant × extension²	$E_e = \dfrac{1}{2}k\,e^2$
period = $\dfrac{1}{\text{frequency}}$	
Ⓗ force on a conductor (at right angles to a magnetic field) carrying a current = magnetic flux density × current × length	$F = B\,I\,l$
change in thermal energy = mass × specific heat capacity × temperature change	$\Delta E = m\,c\,\Delta\theta$
thermal energy for a change of state = mass × specific latent heat	$E = m\,L$
Ⓗ potential difference across primary coil × current in primary coil = potential difference across secondary coil × current in secondary coil	$V_s I_s = V_p I_p$
Ⓗ pressure due to a column of liquid = height of column × density of liquid × gravitational field strength	$p = h\rho g$
Ⓗ $\dfrac{\text{potential difference across primary coil}}{\text{potential difference across secondary coil}}$ $= \dfrac{\text{number of turns in primary coil}}{\text{number of turns in secondary coil}}$	$\dfrac{V_p}{V_s} = \dfrac{n_p}{n_s}$
For gases: pressure × volume = constant	$p\,V = \text{constant}$
Ⓗ force = $\dfrac{\text{change in momentum}}{\text{time taken}}$	$F = \dfrac{m\,\Delta v}{\Delta t}$
magnification = $\dfrac{\text{image height}}{\text{object height}}$	